ARCHITECTS' WORKING DETAILS

ARCHITECTS' WORKING DETAILS

Edited by David Jenkins
and Louis Dezart

The AJ would like to thank John Baxter and Vic Brand for their
drawings; Alan Brookes, John Campbell, Ralph Candappa, Brian
Foster, Lionel Friedland, Roland Gibbard, John Pringle, David
Turnbull and John Winter for their expert guidance; and Peter
Carolin, Colin Davies and Mary Halnan for editorial contributions.

This volume was first published in 1989 by
The Architects' Journal, 9 Queen Anne's Gate, London, SW1H 9BY.
© *The Architects' Journal* 1989

These articles first appeared in *The Architects' Journal.*

ISBN 1 870308 40 9
Printed in the United Kingdom by Diemer and Reynolds, Bedford.

INTRODUCTION

Since September 1988, after a 17-year absence, *The Architects' Journal* has again published a weekly working detail, the best of which are collected in this volume. The first series ran from 1953 to 1971 with the aim of presenting the latest or most novel answers to the perennial problems of architectural detailing.

These details were pored over by architects, cribbed by students or sniffed at by the *cognoscenti*. Many readers made the most of the 'cut out and keep' format and filed these pages away or snapped up the 15 volumes in which they were republished.

In the new series of working details the AJ set out to provide designers not with cribs, but rather a basis on which to study and debate contemporary design, detailing and construction. Each detail, whether new or revisited, is placed in context by reference back to an AJ building feature or study, and accompanied by a detailed commentary backed up by photographs and two full pages of drawings. The details fall under five broad headings: 'External walls and roofs', 'Structure', 'Balconies', 'Staircases', and 'Furniture and fittings'.

The editorial commentaries were written with the assistance of independent experts, and every drawing has been cross-checked where possible with the designers, to whom the AJ is extremely grateful. Their names are given in the contents on the previous page.

It must be emphasised, however, that no working detail illustrated is the ultimate solution to a design problem. These details, invaluable as they are as a reference, should not be interpreted as being any more than that. They are not the modern equivalent of eighteenth century pattern books. Nevertheless, they should enable architects to exchange information on contemporary problems of design. It is then up to the readers to take each drawing as merely indicating a particular stage to which a design problem has been advanced, and to continue that process, refining or modifying it as they go.

CONTENTS

EXTERNAL WALLS AND ROOF
LEISURE POOL
Alsop & Lyall

Sheringham leisure pool has a timber superstructure, a specially developed walling system that is clad in plywood and a proprietary roofing system.

1 Sheringham leisure pool exemplifies the New Spirit in British architecture. In construction terms, it demonstrates that innovation can also be cost effective. It was built for 75-80 per cent of the cost of other pools of comparable size.

The plywood clad timber walling system that forms the external walls of the Sheringham leisure pool 'shed' continues the aesthetic set by the glu-laminated timber primary structure which is expressed on the outside of the building by elongated rafter ends, 1.

The wall build up was developed by the architects and specialist subcontractor. The design process included two consultancy sessions with Trada. The plywood cladding was refined from a single layer to a two layer hardwood WBP build up with a breather membrane located in the ventilated cavity. All timber studding and plywood sheet was double vacuum preservative-treated to give a life expectancy of 60 years. Sheet sizes were a standard $2 \cdot 4$ x $1 \cdot 2$ m—one of the generators of the building's $4 \cdot 8$ m grid.

The panels were factory formed and erected on site in three vertical lifts at the gable ends and a single lift along the long elevations. Real and apparent joints are articulated by applied softwood cover battens, simply pinned over construction butt joints and mastic bedded elsewhere. Horizontal flashings are located at joints between panels. Panel sizes were limited only by trucking and site handling considerations. Joints between the plywood sheets that formed each panel were factory scarf-jointed and bonded with phenolformaldehyde adhesive; sheet edges were epoxy sealed.

The roofing is a patent built up system that

has hitherto been used mainly for light industrial buildings. It offers high thermal and acoustic performance. The complete system is guaranteed for 15 years by the manufacturer.

Further detailed considerations include:
● glu-laminated timber is ideal for a chemically hostile swimming pool environment and has been double vacuum preservative-treated to withstand long-term exposure outside
● all timber inside and outside the building was treated with two coats (plywood has three coats) of microporous exterior grade wood stain giving five to seven years to first maintenance
● long-term maintenance will need to be to a high standard
● softwood framing members reduced initial costs but hardwood offers better long-term performance
● overhanging roofs protect plywood cladding from rainwater and reduce the risk of weather staining.

The plywood cladding is stain finished in alternating bands of brown and grey which give it a striking appearance. Plywood cladding is widely used in Scandinavia, Canada and the US but has been less common in Britain (AJ 16.7.86 p51). Here, as elsewhere, the most important design considerations are selection of the correct grade and edge detailing as this is potentially the most vulnerable part of the sheet. ■

Acknowledgments
The editors acknowledge the help of John Campbell and Lionel Friedland of the Terry Farrell Partnership, formerly of Bickerdike Allen Partners, in the preparation of this article.

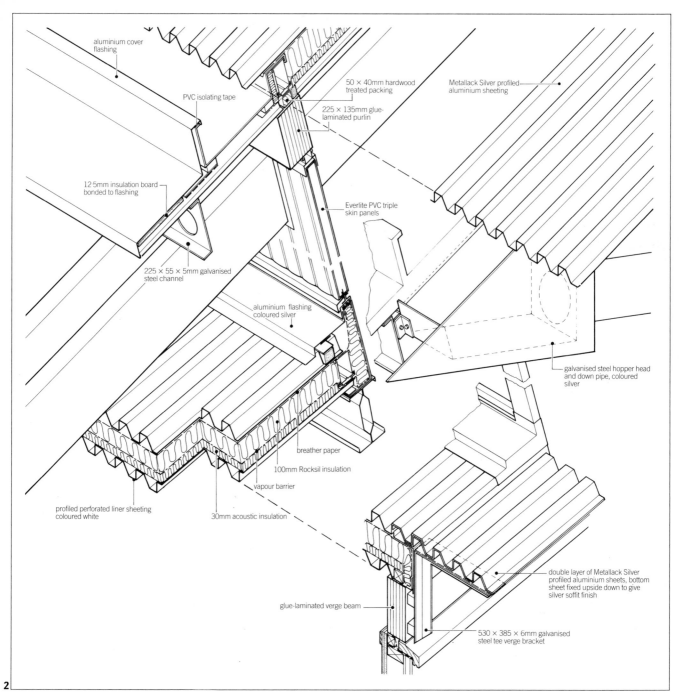

aluminium cover flashing

PVC isolating tape

50 × 40mm hardwood treated packing

Metallack Silver profiled aluminium sheeting

225 × 135mm glue-laminated purlin

12·5mm insulation board bonded to flashing

Everlite PVC triple skin panels

225 × 55 × 5mm galvanised steel channel

aluminium flashing coloured silver

galvanised steel hopper head and down pipe, coloured silver

breather paper

100mm Rocksil insulation

vapour barrier

profiled perforated liner sheeting coloured white

30mm acoustic insulation

double layer of Metallack Silver profiled aluminium sheets, bottom sheet fixed upside down to give silver soffit finish

glue-laminated verge beam

530 × 385 × 6mm galvanised steel tee verge bracket

2

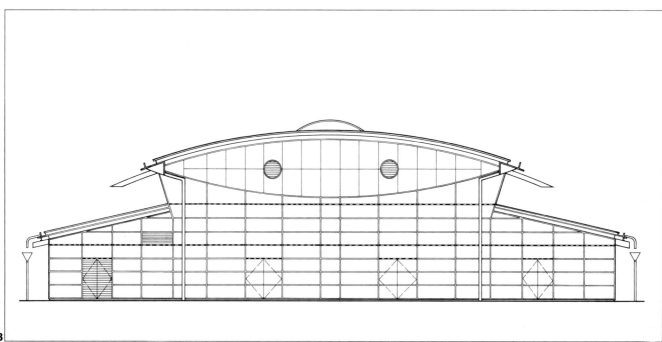

3

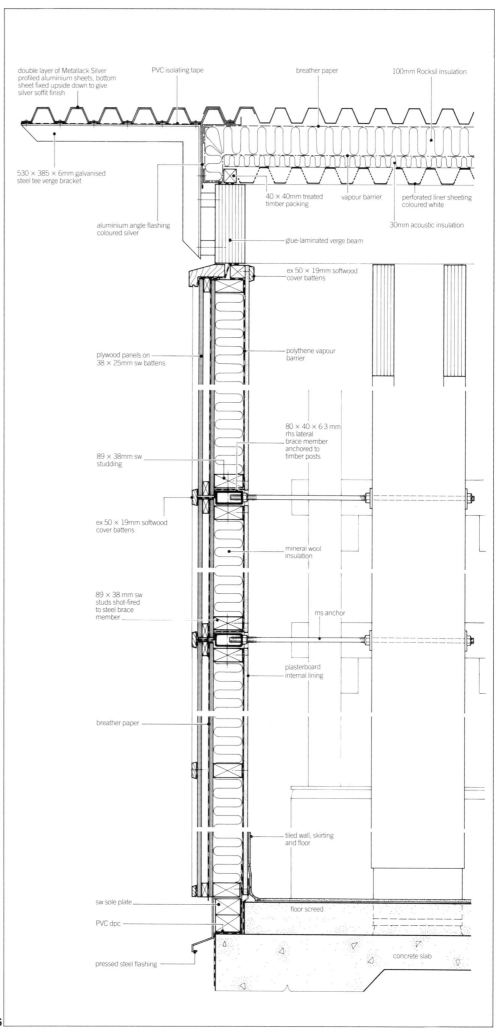

double layer of Metallack Silver profiled aluminium sheets, bottom sheet fixed upside down to give silver soffit finish

PVC isolating tape

breather paper

100mm Rocksil insulation

530 × 385 × 6mm galvanised steel tee verge bracket

aluminium angle flashing coloured silver

40 × 40mm treated timber packing

vapour barrier

perforated liner sheeting coloured white

30mm acoustic insulation

glue-laminated verge beam

ex 50 × 19mm softwood cover battens

plywood panels on 38 × 25mm sw battens

polythene vapour barrier

80 × 40 × 6.3 mm rhs lateral brace member anchored to timber posts

89 × 38mm sw studding

ex 50 × 19mm softwood cover battens

mineral wool insulation

89 × 38 mm sw studs shot-fired to steel brace member

ms anchor

plasterboard internal lining

breather paper

tiled wall, skirting and floor

sw sole plate

floor screed

PVC dpc

concrete slab

pressed steel flashing

2 Axonometric detail at eaves and clerestory of main roof. Rainwater collection is highly inventive in this building. The roofs were detailed to achieve a very thin leading edge. The main roof drains into downpipes which collect water via hoppers at the four corners. The gutter is like the Russian device of having a thin tapered upstand set back from the edge of the roof. Water from the lower side aisle roofs is discharged via tubular gargoyles into free-standing downpipes with conical funnels.
3 End elevation showing the arrangement of walling panels. At the gable ends the panels were erected in three vertical lifts, indicated by the broken lines, and are braced horizontally at these junctions.
4, 5 Site photographs taken during erection of the timber walling.
6 Typical section taken through the centre of a gable end. The decision to construct the external walls in timber was made at an early stage. Timber has the advantages of being relatively cheap and eliminating wet trades above slab level. By being largely prefabricated the system also reduced on-site construction time. The outer plywood skin is of 12·5 mm hardwood WBP ply. The inner skin is of 9·5 mm Canadian sheathing WBP ply.

Credits
location Sheringham, Norfolk
client Clifford Barnett Group for Norfolk District Council
architects William Alsop and John Lyall
project architect Peter Clash
assistant architects Mike Waddington, Simon North, Jonathan Adams, Isabelle Lousada
quantity surveyor Drysdale de Leeuw and Partners
structural engineer Anthony Hunt Associates
management contractor Clugston Construction
roof and rainwater system Belmont Roofing
metalwork R. J. Howlett Engineering
roof sheet supplier Korrugal
external walls Transline

EXTERNAL WALLS
LAW COURTS
Evans and Shalev

The Truro Courts of Justice building has distinctive profiled precast concrete copings, window sills and lintels set against white rough-cast rendered walls.

1 The courthouse viewed from the visitor's car park to the south-east. Precast concrete copings, sills and lintels provide the horizontal emphasis and surface modulation.

Acknowledgment
The editors acknowledge the help of John Campbell and Lionel Friedland, of Terry Farrell Partnership and formerly of Bickerdike Allen Partners, in the preparation of this article.

The building's external appearance is a reinterpretation of the modest vernacular of the adjacent terraced houses, which have rendered walls, simple window openings with projecting sills and gutters and fascias painted in a single colour, to suggest a rudimentary cornice below slate roofs.

External walls are rough-cast rendered and have distinctive raked copings. Band courses of blue/black Staffordshire bricks are placed between wall planes and copings and above window heads to articulate the composition.

The building has an in-situ reinforced concrete frame and floors, formed on standard trough moulds. Walls are of 100 mm concrete block outer leaf and 140 mm thermal insulating block inner leaf with a 50 mm cavity. Wall tiles are stainless steel. Blockwork mortar joints are raked to receive 20 mm render applied in panels. External 'bell-cast' stops, corner beads and movement joint stop beads all have PVC nosings. The aggregate is crushed white marble from a local quarry.

Weepholes and ventilation to cavities is by means of open perpend joints at 800 mm intervals in the brick band courses at top and bottom of walls and above window heads. Flashings and damp-proof courses are lead based and have 200 mm sealed laps.

Copings, sills, lintels and architraves are of precast concrete. Windows are either a patent aluminium frame, double glazed system with a horizontal pivot, or panels of glass blocks. Further detailed considerations include:
● render is divided into panels to prevent cracking caused by thermal movement and to regulate day joints
● copings rely on self weight for vertical restraint and have a minimum 75 per cent weight within the building line. Concealed stainless steel dowel joints at the sides link the coping blocks around the parapet line
● copings are mastic pointed with a nominal 10 mm joint
● all precast concrete elements are painted with a white high-build microporous copolymer resin emulsion that contains fungicides to reduce algae growth, giving a minimum of five years to first maintenance
● long lintels above glass block panels in the rotunda lanterns are relieved by 150 x 120 x 10 mm continuous stainless steel angles bolted to the in-situ reinforced concrete downstand beam
● overhanging copings protect render from rainwater and reduce the possible risk of weather staining.

Generally the materials used are of proven durability. But precast concrete window sills, lintels and architraves, if continued to the inside of the wall, can form cold bridges and lead to condensation. Particular attention to the positioning of dpc's and flashings is essential to ensure that rain water is thrown off at window openings and parapets. ■

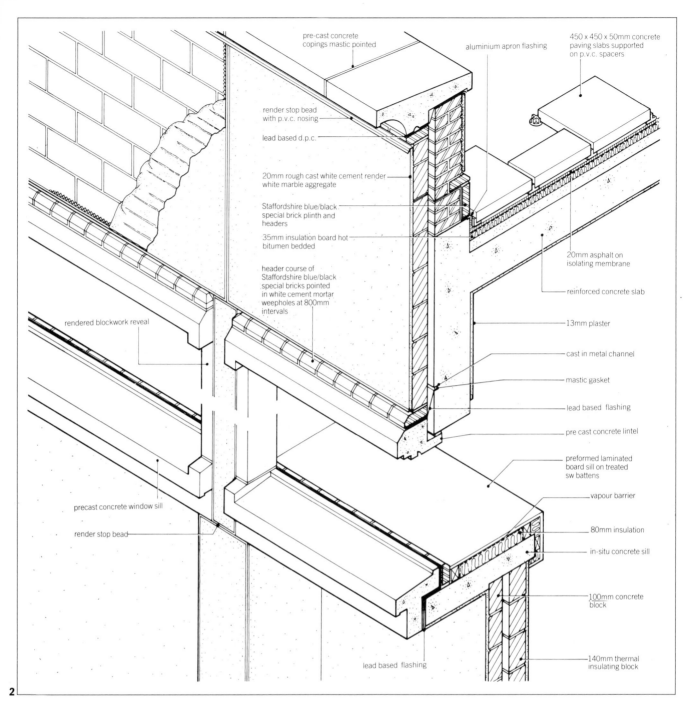

pre-cast concrete copings mastic pointed

aluminium apron flashing

450 x 450 x 50mm concrete paving slabs supported on p.v.c. spacers

render stop bead with p.v.c. nosing

lead based d.p.c.

20mm rough cast white cement render white marble aggregate

Staffordshire blue/black special brick plinth and headers

35mm insulation board hot bitumen bedded

header course of Staffordshire blue/black special bricks pointed in white cement mortar weepholes at 800mm intervals

rendered blockwork reveal

precast concrete window sill

render stop bead

20mm asphalt on isolating membrane

reinforced concrete slab

13mm plaster

cast in metal channel

mastic gasket

lead based flashing

pre cast concrete lintel

preformed laminated board sill on treated sw battens

vapour barrier

80mm insulation

in-situ concrete sill

100mm concrete block

140mm thermal insulating block

lead based flashing

2

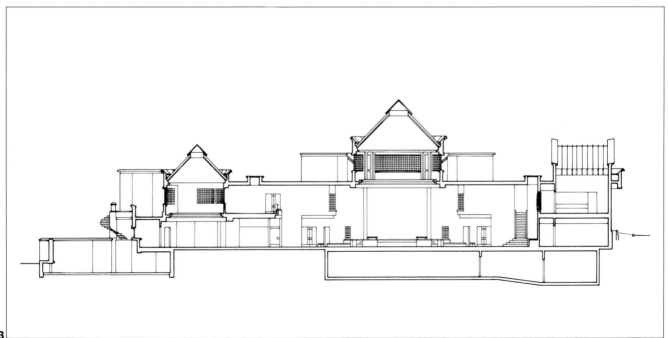

3

2 Isometric section through roof terrace, external wall and window on the north elevation.
3 North/south section through the public concourse.
4 View of north elevation.
5 Construction photograph showing build-up of external render and arrangement of stop-beads.
6 Section through external walls and roof terrace. Precast window sills are propped during construction and secured by the weight of masonry built up at their ends.

Credits
location Edward Street, Truro.
architects Evans and Shalev; Eldred Evans, David Shalev, Charles Mador
quantity surveyor MDA; Richard Pope, Kevin Heaton
structural engineer Anthony Hunt Associates; Stephen Morley, Alan Smith
services engineer Max Fordham and partners, Max Fordham, David Lindsay
contractor Dudley Coles Ltd
contract manager Bryan Hammond
site agent Tony Luke
clerk of works Wilf Ballm
project managers Property Services Agency, Martin Brooks, John Whiting, Jim Dunaway, Len Froom-Lewis
sealants G L Mastics, Bristol
precast concrete products W J Ladd, Redruth
concrete blocks ECC, St Austell
insulating blocks Plasmor Ltd
windows and external doors Schuco windows, supplied and fixed by James Gibbons.

Photo credit
Photographs by Martin Charles.

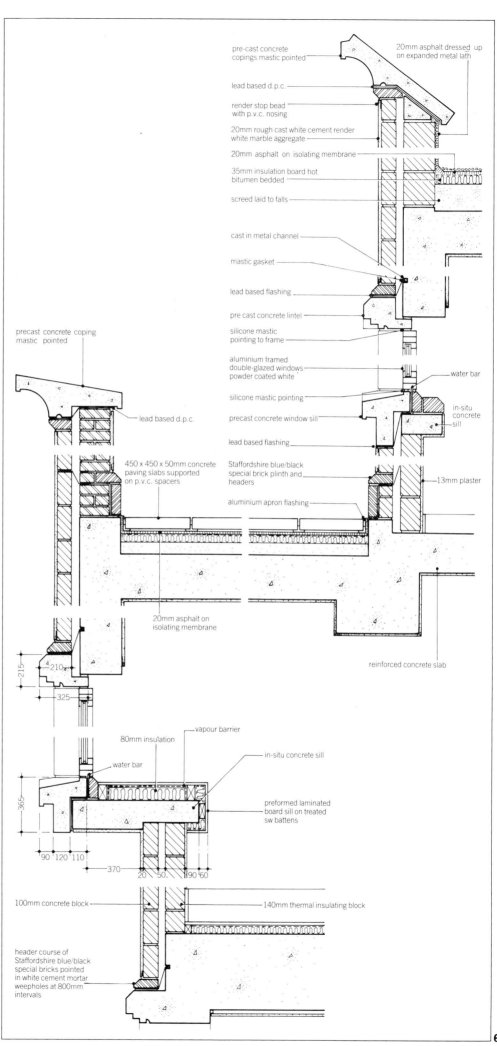

pre-cast concrete copings mastic pointed
20mm asphalt dressed up on expanded metal lath
lead based d.p.c.
render stop bead with p.v.c. nosing
20mm rough cast white cement render white marble aggregate
20mm asphalt on isolating membrane
35mm insulation board hot bitumen bedded
screed laid to falls
cast in metal channel
mastic gasket
lead based flashing
pre cast concrete lintel
silicone mastic pointing to frame
aluminium framed double-glazed windows powder coated white
water bar
silicone mastic pointing
precast concrete window sill
in-situ concrete sill
lead based flashing
precast concrete coping mastic pointed
lead based d.p.c.
450 x 450 x 50mm concrete paving slabs supported on p.v.c. spacers
Staffordshire blue/black special brick plinth and headers
13mm plaster
aluminium apron flashing
20mm asphalt on isolating membrane
reinforced concrete slab
215
210
325
vapour barrier
80mm insulation
in-situ concrete sill
water bar
365
preformed laminated board sill on treated sw battens
90 120 110
370
20 50 90 60
100mm concrete block
140mm thermal insulating block
header course of Staffordshire blue/black special bricks pointed in white cement mortar weepholes at 800mm intervals

EXTERNAL WALLS AND ROOF
PUMPING STATION
John Outram Associates

The Isle of Dogs pumping station is steel-framed and has external walls of polychromatic brickwork with precast concrete decorative components. The roof is of glazed pantiles.

1

1 The building viewed from the riverside. Giant order columns with precast concrete capitals conceal ventilation ducts.

Acknowledgment
The editors acknowledge the help of John Campbell and Lionel Friedland of the Terry Farrell Partnership, formerly of Bickerdike Allen Partners, in the preparation of this article.

The station pumps all surface water from the Isle of Dogs. Under storm overflow conditions it handles combined flows of water and sewage, so the building is vigorously ventilated through electrically operated fans in the pediments and circular grilles in the long elevations to avoid a build-up of methane gas. Water and sewage is regulated by a system of pumps through underground chambers and eventually discharges into the Thames. The building is operated by remote control. As it is unmanned and unheated no insulation was required.

The building is a steel-framed structure above massive concrete groundworks. Steel columns are encased in concrete for fire protection and clad in brickwork. External walls are of bands of contrasting brickwork. The roof is covered with green glazed Roman tiles on battens and counter-battens over diagonal T&G boarding nailed to timber joists.

At each end of the building, paired giant order semicircular columns conceal ventilation ducts. Painted precast concrete fins, 2 metres high, form huge stylised Corinthian capitals.

Precast elements (AJ 9.12.87 p53) are of acid etched concrete, some self-coloured black, some painted either during manufacture or once fixed on site. Stainless steel fixing sockets or wall tiles are cast-in and the components either bolted to the steel frame or built into the brickwork. Cramps and ties are

of stainless steel. The 'daisy' profile columns on the long elevations were cast in three horizontal sections and spaced apart by a self-coloured black unit to avoid the problem of precise alignment.

The brickwork is of Staffordshire blue engineering bricks to dado level with bands of Butterley 'Rochford' red facing bricks and Redland 'Otterham' yellow stock bricks above.

Further detailed considerations include:
● high alumina cement was used for the self-coloured precast units. It is darker than opc, and when mixed with Belgian marble aggregate and pigment gives a deep black finish that only requires clear lacquering. These elements are mainly decorative and have no structural role
● microporous acrylic paint was applied to precast concrete elements in one matt colour coat and two clear lacquer coats
● gutters and pediment fascias are of predrilled hot-dip galvanised mild steel, polyester powder-coated and fixed with stainless steel bolts. Gaskets and washers are of neoprene.

The brickwork is tied to the concrete column casings with cast-in stainless steel ties. Outram has not provided vertical expansion joints in the brickwork, relying instead on soft lime mortar mixes and the returns in the brickwork piers around the columns to avoid accumulated incremental thermal expansion along the length of the wall. ■

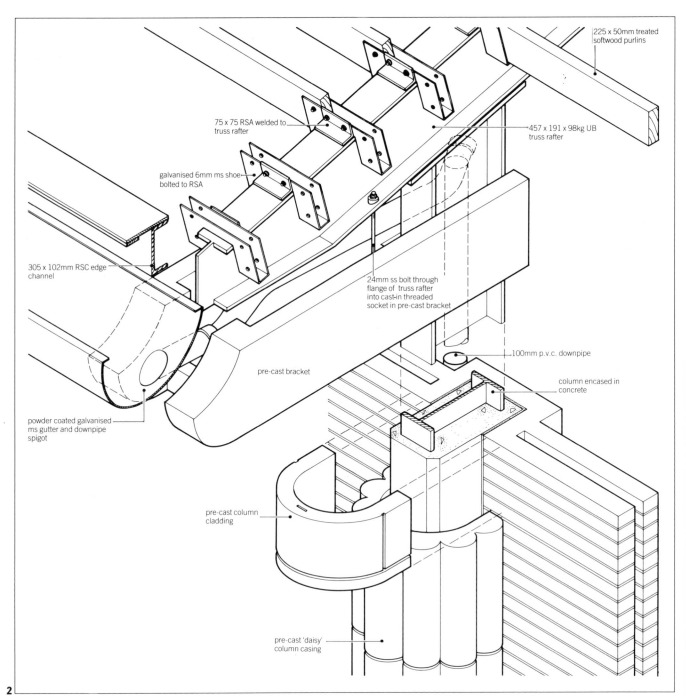

225 x 50mm treated
softwood purlins

75 x 75 RSA welded to
truss rafter

457 x 191 x 98kg UB
truss rafter

galvanised 6mm ms shoe
bolted to RSA

305 x 102mm RSC edge
channel

24mm ss bolt through
flange of truss rafter
into cast-in threaded
socket in pre-cast bracket

pre-cast bracket

100mm p.v.c. downpipe

column encased in
concrete

powder coated galvanised
ms gutter and downpipe
spigot

pre-cast column
cladding

pre-cast 'daisy'
column casing

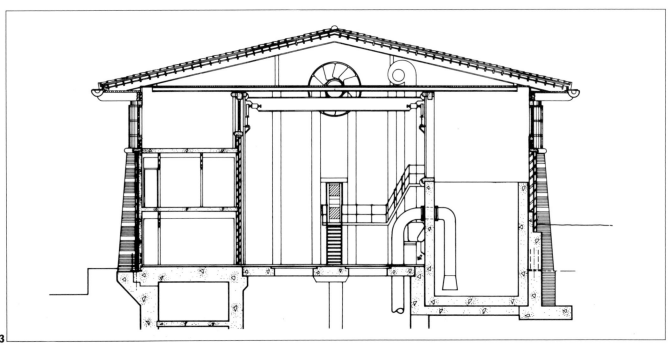

2 Cut-away isometric of the eaves assembly showing the build-up of concrete, brick and precast cladding around the steel structure.
3 Section through the pump hall.
4, 5 Details at the eaves showing the precast brackets which are suspended from the structural steelwork on stainless steel bolts at the eaves and mid-points.
6 Detailed section through external wall and eaves.

Credits
location Stewart Street, Isle of Dogs, London E14
client London Docklands Development Corporation/Thames Water Authority
architects John Outram Associates
project architects John Outram, Helen Pedder
assistant architects Graham Anderson, Jonathan Hill
civil, structural and executive engineers Sir William Halcrow and Partners
service engineer Lewin Fryer and Partners
quantity surveyor Michael F. Edwards and Associates
main contractor Peter Birse
gutters and cladding Airdale Engineering
precast concrete Diespeker
steel frame Hamilton Slade
roof tiles AVH Interbrick
electrical fans Davidson & Company
metal fabrication Brentford Steel Fabrications
fan cowling Commercial Fibreglass Mouldings
pavings Charcon
blue bricks Ketley Brick Company
red bricks Butterley Ltd
yellow stocks Redland Ltd
brown bricks Hawkins Ltd.

Photo credit
Photographs by Charlotte Wood.

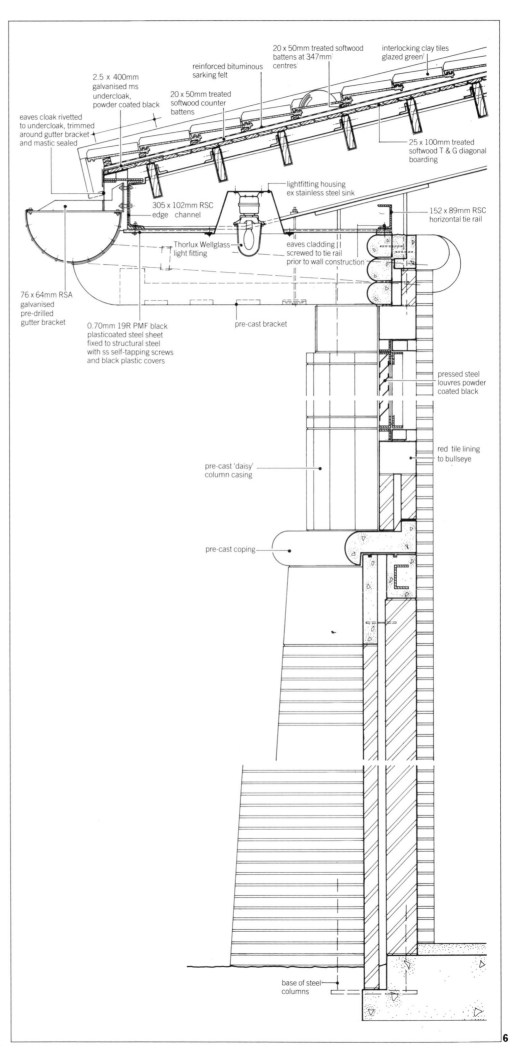

2.5 x 400mm galvanised ms undercloak, powder coated black

reinforced bituminous sarking felt

20 x 50mm treated softwood battens at 347mm centres

interlocking clay tiles glazed green

20 x 50mm treated softwood counter battens

eaves cloak rivetted to undercloak, trimmed around gutter bracket and mastic sealed

25 x 100mm treated softwood T & G diagonal boarding

lightfitting housing ex stainless steel sink

305 x 102mm RSC edge channel

152 x 89mm RSC horizontal tie rail

Thorlux Wellglass light fitting

eaves cladding screwed to tie rail prior to wall construction

76 x 64mm RSA galvanised pre-drilled gutter bracket

0.70mm 19R PMF black plasticoated steel sheet fixed to structural steel with ss self-tapping screws and black plastic covers

pre-cast bracket

pressed steel louvres powder coated black

pre-cast 'daisy' column casing

red tile lining to bullseye

pre-cast coping

base of steel columns

EXTERNAL WALLS AND ROOF
RECORDING EQUIPMENT FACTORY
Michael Hopkins and Partners.

The Solid State Logic factory has fully glazed external walls with external motorised Venetian blinds. The roof is a single-layer polymeric membrane over insulation on metal decking.

1

1 External blinds at first floor level are restrained in guide wires and prevented from lowering in high winds by a wind speed sensor on the roof. Blinds automatically retract at night.

Acknowledgment
The editors acknowledge the help of John Campbell and Lionel Friedland of Farrell and Co, formerly of Bickerdike Allen Partners, in the preparation of this article.

The choice of full-height double glazing for the elevations was determined by visual and thermal parameters. The glazing allows a direct relationship with the surrounding garden. High illuminance from natural light and solar radiant heat (up to a limit) will offset lighting and heating costs at certain times of the year.

A grey tint in the glass moderates solar heat gain but tends to mask the views in and out, reducing the building's transparency. Excessive solar heat gain is prevented by fully retractable, remote-controlled, external blinds mounted between subsidiary columns on the first floor elevations.

Blinds are set automatically on a timer switch and can be adjusted to cope with the changing sun path. A cantilevered first floor provides permanent shading from high summer sun to the ground floor. Services engineer's calculations show peak summertime temperatures within the building (possibly two to three days per year) in the region of 29°C for open-plan areas rising to 31°C in cellular accommodation.

Natural ventilation is provided by full-height sliding glazed doors opening on to shallow balconies which allow 50 per cent of the perimeter to be opened up. The building is also mechanically vented (AJ 26.10.88 p61) but not air-conditioned.

Potential condensation on steel subframing and down-draughts at the glazing are offset by the location of heating convectors in trenches around the perimeter of the building on both floors. These counter heat losses where they occur and prevent large temperature variations within the building.

Total heat losses are well within the limits set by the Building Regulations. Given such a deep plan, the walls play a small part in heat loss calculations. The major factor—the roof—is highly insulated, achieving a U-value of $0 \cdot 2\,W/m^2K$.

Further detailed considerations include:
● anticipated long-term mid-span sag of up to 20 mm at the first floor slab cantilever requires a flexible horizontal weathertight junction between slab, edge beam, and glazing elements which rely on compressible packing between steel and concrete
● supplementary external columns on the first floor, which brace the glazing, are pin-jointed. Movement under wind lift at the eaves is accommodated by sliding joints at the window head framing
● steel window subframing and roof drainage pipes form cold bridges—constant air movement should prevent condensation forming.

The building relies almost entirely on proprietary products and systems. Construction was broken down into clearly defined subcontract packages, the only major in-situ element being the first floor coffered concrete slab. ∎

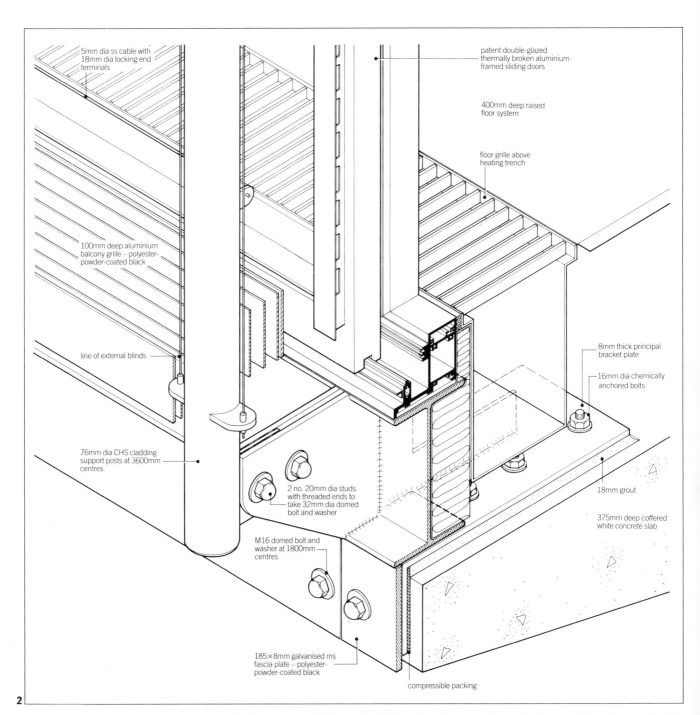

5mm dia ss cable with
18mm dia locking end
terminals

patent double-glazed
thermally broken aluminium-
framed sliding doors

400mm deep raised
floor system

floor grille above
heating trench

100mm deep aluminium
balcony grille – polyester-
powder-coated black

line of external blinds

8mm thick principal
bracket plate

16mm dia chemically
anchored bolts

76mm dia CHS cladding
support posts at 3600mm
centres

2 no. 20mm dia studs
with threaded ends to
take 32mm dia domed
bolt and washer

18mm grout

375mm deep coffered
white concrete slab

M16 domed bolt and
washer at 1800mm
centres

185×8mm galvanised ms
fascia plate – polyester-
powder-coated black

compressible packing

2

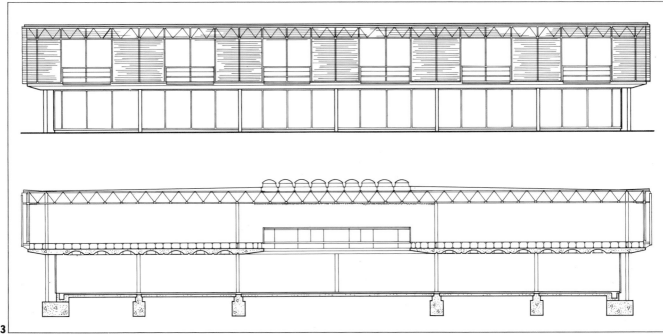

3

4

2 Isometric detail at first floor
slab edge.
3 Elevation and cross-section.
4 The ground floor is shaded by the
overhanging first floor.
5 Section through roof, external
glazing and blinds at first
floor level.

Credits
location Springhill Road, Begbroke,
Oxon
client Solid State Logic
architect Michael Hopkins and
Partners
partners in charge Michael Hopkins,
Ian Sharratt
project architect Peter Romaniuk
assistant architects Peter Cartwright,
Bill Dunster, Graham Saunders
quantity surveyor Davis Langdon and
Everest, Alec Waller, Clive Lewis
structural and services engineer Buro
Happold, M. Dickson, Michael Green,
Peter Moseley
main contractor Walter Lawrence
Project Management
project manager Peter Richardson
spacedeck Spacedecks
steelwork Allway and Browne
fire protection Fireguard
in-situ concrete Whelan and Grant
louvre blinds Technical Blinds
raised floors Floorplan Electrical
ceilings Diespecker
metalwork Burroughs Engineering
groundworks Talon Construction
roof and rooflights Midland Single Pry
rooflight supplier William Cox
roof membrane supplier Sarnafil
cladding S B Systems
cladding supplier Schuco
International

Photo credit
Photography by Martin Charles

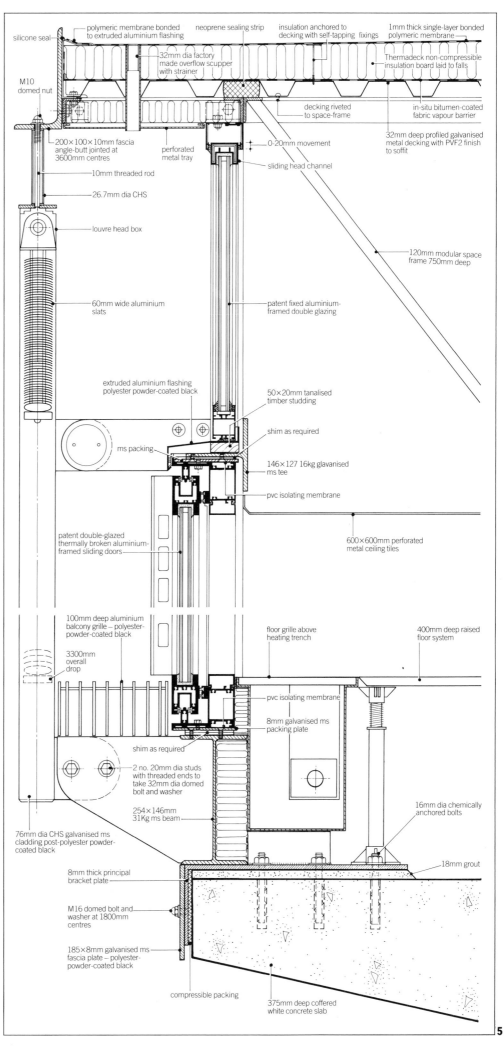

silicone seal
polymeric membrane bonded to extruded aluminium flashing
neoprene sealing strip
insulation anchored to decking with self-tapping fixings
1mm thick single-layer bonded polymeric membrane
M10 domed nut
32mm dia factory made overflow scupper with strainer
Thermadeck non-compressible insulation board laid to falls
decking riveted to space-frame
in-situ bitumen-coated fabric vapour barrier
200×100×10mm fascia angle-butt jointed at 3600mm centres
perforated metal tray
0-20mm movement
32mm deep profiled galvanised metal decking with PVF2 finish to soffit
10mm threaded rod
sliding head channel
26.7mm dia CHS
louvre head box
120mm modular space frame 750mm deep
60mm wide aluminium slats
patent fixed aluminium-framed double glazing
extruded aluminium flashing polyester powder-coated black
50×20mm tanalised timber studding
shim as required
ms packing
146×127 16kg glavanised ms tee
pvc isolating membrane
patent double-glazed thermally broken aluminium-framed sliding doors
600×600mm perforated metal ceiling tiles
100mm deep aluminium balcony grille – polyester-powder-coated black
floor grille above heating trench
400mm deep raised floor system
3300mm overall drop
pvc isolating membrane
8mm galvanised ms packing plate
shim as required
2 no. 20mm dia studs with threaded ends to take 32mm dia domed bolt and washer
254×146mm 31Kg ms beam
16mm dia chemically anchored bolts
76mm dia CHS galvanised ms cladding post-polyester powder-coated black
18mm grout
8mm thick principal bracket plate
M16 domed bolt and washer at 1800mm centres
185×8mm galvanised ms fascia plate – polyester-powder-coated black
compressible packing
375mm deep coffered white concrete slab

5

EXTERNAL WALLS
LAW COURTS
YRM Partnership

Manchester Magistrates Courts' precise white frame, set against bronze glass, marked the high point of YRM's tile style when it was completed in 1971.

1 The main entrance elevation to Crown Square—a civic space defined by legal buildings. The structural frame is simply expressed to describe the relationship between three floors of double-height courtrooms in the centre of the plan with six floors of office and ancillary accommodation at the east and west ends. Cells and plant rooms are located on the top floors.

Acknowledgment
The editors acknowledge the help of John Campbell of Farrell and Company, formerly of Bickerdike Allen Partners, and Lionel Friedland in the preparation of this article.

The courts and office accommodation are contained within a rectangular plan (70·1 m × 42·7 m) on three main floors above an external podium which covers the whole site. The building has an in-situ concrete frame clad externally in 200 × 50 mm white glazed ceramic tiles.

Unlike many tile-clad examples of this period, the building has not shed its tiles and, though it now needs cleaning, still looks crisp. Generally the building has worn well, but due to the often simplistic (or optimistic) nature of '70s detailing and the limitations of some materials, there are some weaknesses:
● water run-off at joints between horizontal tiles causes staining and lichen growth on the mortar below
● lack of an edge drip detail on tiled soffits has led to staining from wind-blown rain-water.

The ceramic tiles are fully mortar-bedded on the bush-hammered concrete frame. There is no evidence of salt deposit staining, usually the first symptom of water penetration of the substrate. In this case, the heavy concrete construction acts as a heat sink, effectively regulating differential thermal movement between the tiles and mortar bed which can otherwise loosen the tiles.

Polysulphide pointing to the expansion joints is at the end of its 10-to-15-year life and shows signs of slumping. The heavy reliance on such joints between original subcontract works (tiling, window frames, etc) could lead to future water penetration if the sealant is not replaced soon.

The aluminium window-framing subcontract drawings indicate a general reliance on steel subframing and corner angle reinforcement with no separation material between metals. Galvanised steelwork was additionally red-lead-primed to avoid bimetallic action, and there is no outward evidence of long-term corrosion. Without dismantling a section of framing, no definite conclusions can be drawn, but this method is today considered to be bad practice.

There is extensive cold bridging in the aluminium window framing and the building is wholly single-glazed in 8 mm or 12 mm solar bronze glass, which, pre-energy-crisis, was thought to be sufficient. Thermally broken framing sections were not common at the time. Perimeter heating and large-volume air movement reduce the risk of condensation.

The building maintenance department reports that water is leaking into the basement car park. This could be caused by failure of the asphalt below the concrete terrace pavings or the clogging of open drainage joints between the slabs, which has led to the build-up of standing water. No leakage problems have been reported elsewhere in the building which could be better maintained, but still seems to be in remarkably good shape. ∎

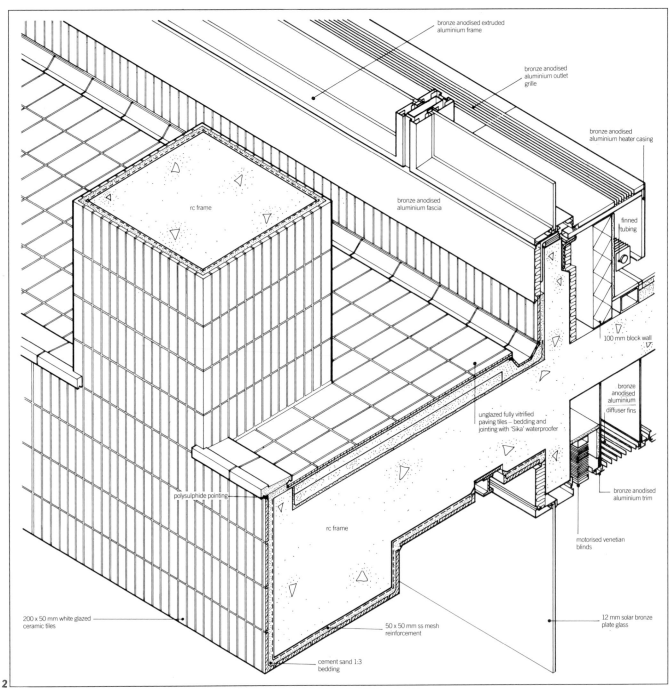

bronze anodised extruded aluminium frame

bronze anodised aluminium outlet grille

bronze anodised aluminium heater casing

bronze anodised aluminium fascia

finned tubing

rc frame

100 mm block wall

bronze anodised aluminium diffuser fins

unglazed fully vitrified paving tiles — bedding and jointing with 'Sika' waterproofer

bronze anodised aluminium trim

polysulphide pointing

rc frame

motorised venetian blinds

12 mm solar bronze plate glass

200 x 50 mm white glazed ceramic tiles

50 x 50 mm ss mesh reinforcement

cement sand 1:3 bedding

2

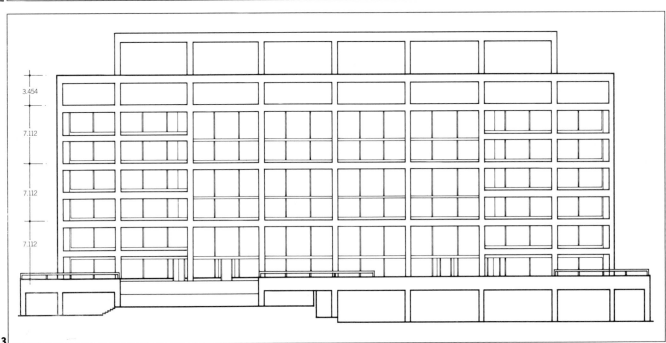

3.454

7.112

7.112

7.112

3

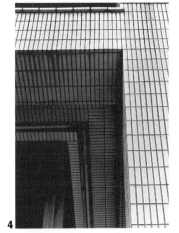

2 Isometric detail of the tile-clad frame.
3 Elevation to Crown Square.
4, 5 Photographs taken in November 1988, 4, and shortly after completion in September 1971, 5. Tile-clad soffits and frame faces have suffered superficial staining which could be easily cleaned off. Joints between paving slabs on the podium, 5, have become blocked due to lack of maintenance which has led to the build-up of surface water.
6 Section through the external glazing and expressed frame.

Credits
location Crown Square, Manchester
client City of Manchester
architects YRM Partnership (formerly Yorke Rosenberg Mardall) in association with S. G. Besant Roberts, city architect
quantity surveyor T. Sumner Smith and Partners
services engineer Zisman Bowyer and Partners
structural engineer Mathews and Mumby
acoustic consultant Sandy Brown Associates

Photo credit
Photographs 1, 4 by Charlotte Wood; 5 by Richard Einzig.

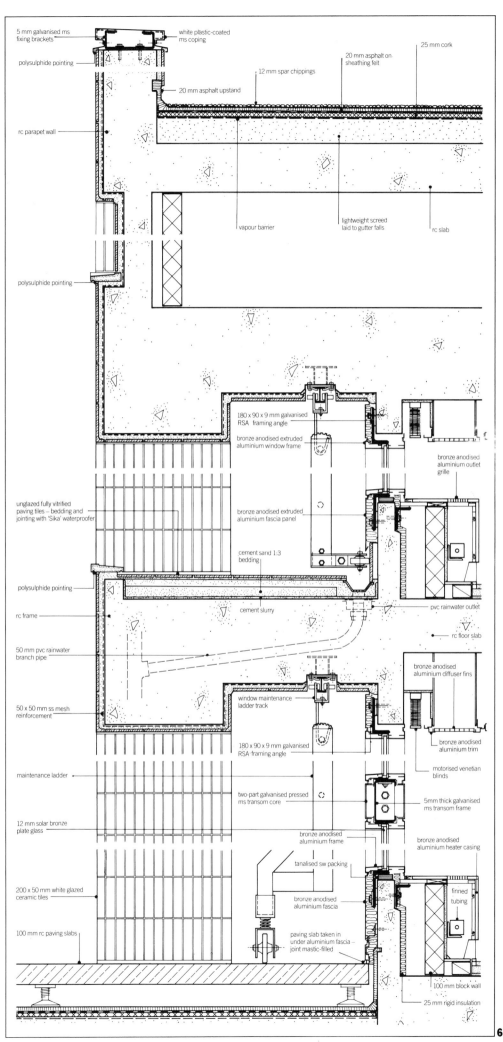

5 mm galvanised ms fixing brackets

white plastic-coated ms coping

polysulphide pointing

20 mm asphalt upstand

12 mm spar chippings

20 mm asphalt on sheathing felt

25 mm cork

rc parapet wall

vapour barrier

lightweight screed laid to gutter falls

rc slab

polysulphide pointing

180 x 90 x 9 mm galvanised RSA framing angle

bronze anodised extruded aluminium window frame

bronze anodised aluminium outlet grille

unglazed fully vitrified paving tiles – bedding and jointing with 'Sika' waterproofer

bronze anodised extruded aluminium fascia panel

cement sand 1:3 bedding

polysulphide pointing

cement slurry

pvc rainwater outlet

rc frame

rc floor slab

50 mm pvc rainwater branch pipe

bronze anodised aluminium diffuser fins

window maintenance ladder track

50 x 50 mm ss mesh reinforcement

180 x 90 x 9 mm galvanised RSA framing angle

bronze anodised aluminium trim

motorised venetian blinds

maintenance ladder

two-part galvanised pressed ms transom core

5mm thick galvanised ms transom frame

12 mm solar bronze plate glass

bronze anodised aluminium frame

bronze anodised aluminium heater casing

tanalised sw packing

200 x 50 mm white glazed ceramic tiles

bronze anodised aluminium fascia

finned tubing

100 mm rc paving slabs

paving slab taken in under aluminium fascia – joint mastic-filled

100 mm block wall

25 mm rigid insulation

EXTERNAL WALLS
OFFICES
Rolfe Judd

The stone-faced
precast cladding
system for offices in the
City of London
conservation area was
designed to achieve the
appearance of a
traditionally
constructed building.

1

**1 The cladding system was adopted
for speed of erection without the
need for perimeter scaffolding. The
cladding period allowed by the
client's programme was only 15½
weeks as opposed to an estimated
28 weeks for conventionally fixed
stonework on a brick or blockwork
backing. Allocating a cladding-zone
depth early in the design process
allowed decisions on the structural
steel frame and groundworks to be
finalised while the detailed design
of the facades continued. Panels
were erected by crane and
silicone-jointing applied from a
cherry-picker platform.**

Acknowledgment
The editors acknowledge the help of
John Campbell of Terry Farrell &
Company and Lionel Friedland of
Pentarch in the preparation of
this article.

Each of the elevations comprises a number of
Portland-stone-faced concrete panels; the
largest is 3.65m × 4.20 m and incorporates
window openings. The panels were made
up in timber moulds with the 60 mm thick
stone slabs acting as permanent shuttering
for a nominally 150 mm thick reinforced
concrete substructure.

The stonework is secured to the concrete by
6 mm stainless steel dowels, at alternating
45° angles, epoxy-grouted into holes let into
the slabs. To allow for differential movement,
a debonding agent was applied to the back of
the stone and rubber grommets were fitted
over the stainless steel dowels prior to
casting. Stonework joints within the panels
are 6 mm wide and grouted with white cement
lime mortar. Joints between panels are
nominally 16 mm wide, silicone-sealed on the
outer face, with a secondary inner seal of
compressed bituminised polyurethane.

Restraint fixings at top and bottom are by
means of stainless steel bolts into threaded
sockets cast into the back of the panels. These
are secured by bolting through angle brackets
welded to the steel frame. Enlarged holes in
the angle brackets allow for tolerance.

The panels are constructed with concrete
lugs on the bottom of the inside face which
provide a seating into the steel frame. A
rectangular hole within the lug is located over
an angle bracket welded to the top flange of
the supporting beam. The lug is temporarily

supported by shims to allow the panel to be
positioned for line and level, and this tolerance
gap is then grouted up. Non-standard panels
are fixed as appropriate.

Further detailed considerations include:
● the system is based on two-stage sealed
joints. The first stage acts as a rain barrier,
the second as an air and water seal. If the first
seal breaks down, gusts of wind could cause a
pressure differential across the external seal,
subjecting the inner seal to the full external
pressure which it may not be able to resist
● there is no method of dealing with water
trapped between two seals from either the
failure of the first seal or from soaking
through the porous stone and running down
the debonded stone and concrete interface
● there is a foil vapour barrier on the rear of
the plasterboard dry-lining. Discontinuity or
perforations in the vapour barrier may result
in condensation on the rear of the concrete
panel. However, there is no provision for
collecting and draining out any condensate or
for ventilating the cavity between the
cladding panel and the insulated dry-lining.

This cladding system has the advantage of
achieving the appearance of traditionally laid
ashlar stonework and is quickly erected
without scaffolding. But weighed against this
is the relatively short life-span of the silicone
sealants on which its success depends, the
first inspection having been specified to take
place after 15 years. ■

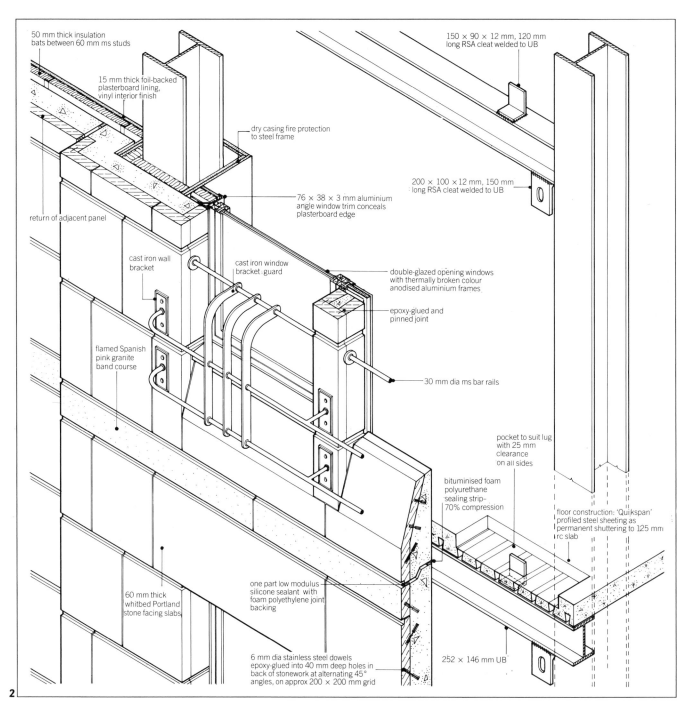

50 mm thick insulation bats between 60 mm ms studs

15 mm thick foil-backed plasterboard lining, vinyl interior finish

dry casing fire protection to steel frame

150 × 90 × 12 mm, 120 mm long RSA cleat welded to UB

76 × 38 × 3 mm aluminium angle window trim conceals plasterboard edge

200 × 100 × 12 mm, 150 mm long RSA cleat welded to UB

return of adjacent panel

cast iron wall bracket

cast iron window bracket guard

double-glazed opening windows with thermally broken colour anodised aluminium frames

epoxy-glued and pinned joint

flamed Spanish pink granite band course

30 mm dia ms bar rails

pocket to suit lug with 25 mm clearance on all sides

bituminised foam polyurethane sealing strip– 70% compression

floor construction: 'Quikspan' profiled steel sheeting as permanent shuttering to 125 mm rc slab

60 mm thick whitbed Portland stone facing slabs

one part low modulus silicone sealant with foam polyethylene joint backing

6 mm dia stainless steel dowels epoxy-glued into 40 mm deep holes in back of stonework at alternating 45° angles, on approx 200 × 200 mm grid

252 × 146 mm UB

2

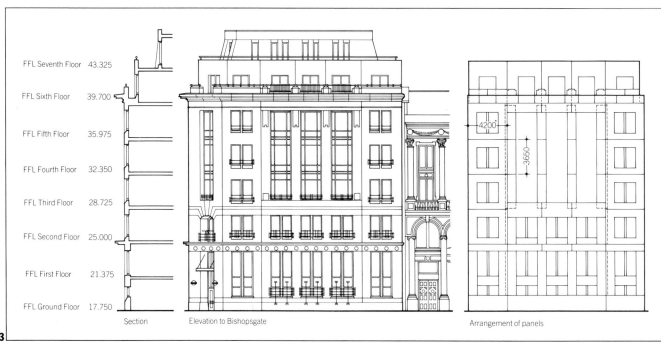

FFL Seventh Floor	43.325
FFL Sixth Floor	39.700
FFL Fifth Floor	35.975
FFL Fourth Floor	32.350
FFL Third Floor	28.725
FFL Second Floor	25.000
FFL First Floor	21.375
FFL Ground Floor	17.750

Section

Elevation to Bishopsgate

4200

3650

Arrangement of panels

3

2 Cut-away isometric of panel at second-floor level showing fixings to structural steelwork. The aluminium window-frames were fitted to the backs of the panels after erection.
3 Section and elevation of Bishopsgate showing arrangements of prefabricated panels.
4, 5 Elevation to Bishopsgate and detail of panel joint at cornice level. Horizontal panel joints coincide with the recessed bands in the rustication and are hard to spot. Vertical joints generally occur at the returns in the elevation modelling and are less discreet.
6 Section through a typical cladding panel at second-floor level. There are no drained joints, dpcs, baffles or flashings between panels.

Credits
location 62 Cornhill, London EC3
client Greycoat plc
architects Rolfe Judd
directors in charge David Rolfe, Richard Dickinson (design), Michael Trickett (construction)
project architect Robert Brown
quantity surveyor V. J. Mendoza and Partners
mechanical and electrical engineers J. Roger Preston and Partners
structural engineer Andrews Kent and Stone
management contractor Woolf Construction Management
superstructure concrete and groundworks Swift Structures
steelwork, Holorib floor decking Booth Steelwork
stone-faced precast cladding panels Minsterstone
window/glazing installation Solaglas
partitions/dry-lining installation Circle Industries (UK)
metalwork Beaver Building Systems

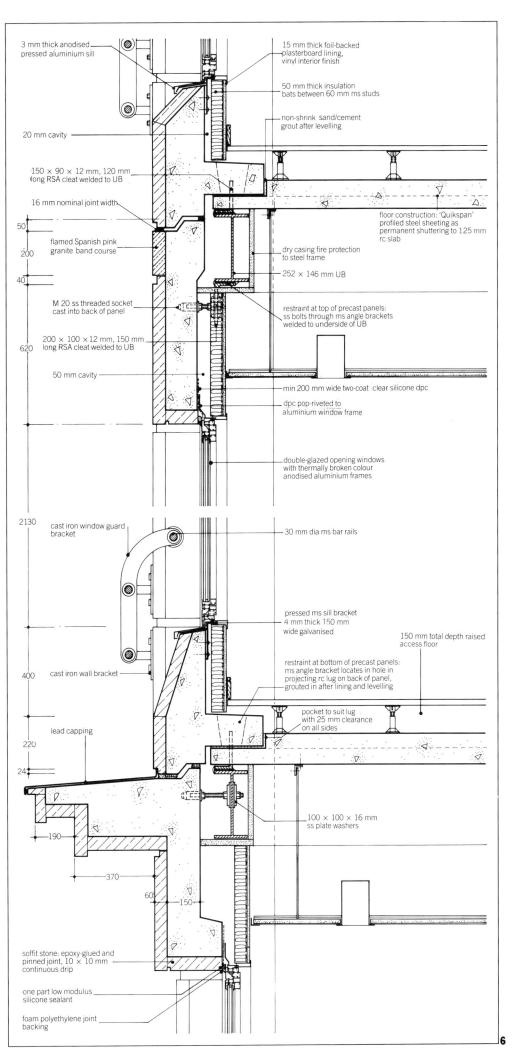

3 mm thick anodised pressed aluminium sill

15 mm thick foil-backed plasterboard lining, vinyl interior finish

50 mm thick insulation bats between 60 mm ms studs

non-shrink sand/cement grout after levelling

20 mm cavity

150 × 90 × 12 mm, 120 mm long RSA cleat welded to UB

16 mm nominal joint width

floor construction: 'Quikspan' profiled steel sheeting as permanent shuttering to 125 mm rc slab

50

200

flamed Spanish pink granite band course

dry casing fire protection to steel frame

40

252 × 146 mm UB

M 20 ss threaded socket cast into back of panel

restraint at top of precast panels: ss bolts through ms angle brackets welded to underside of UB

200 × 100 × 12 mm, 150 mm long RSA cleat welded to UB

620

50 mm cavity

min 200 mm wide two-coat clear silicone dpc

dpc pop-riveted to aluminium window frame

double-glazed opening windows with thermally broken colour anodised aluminium frames

2130

cast iron window guard bracket

30 mm dia ms bar rails

pressed ms sill bracket 4 mm thick 150 mm wide galvanised

150 mm total depth raised access floor

400

cast iron wall bracket

restraint at bottom of precast panels: ms angle bracket locates in hole in projecting rc lug on back of panel, grouted in after lining and levelling

pocket to suit lug with 25 mm clearance on all sides

lead capping

220

24

190

100 × 100 × 16 mm ss plate washers

370

60

150

soffit stone: epoxy-glued and pinned joint, 10 × 10 mm continuous drip

one part low modulus silicone sealant

foam polyethylene joint backing

EXTERNAL WALLS AND ROOF
PRIMARY SCHOOL
Hampshire County Architects

Yateley Newlands Primary School, first occupied in December 1980, is an energy-efficient building that uses traditional methods of climate control.

1 The building is traditionally constructed from predominantly natural materials: brick walls, timber structure and window frames, with concrete roof tiles. External finishes such as the timber soffit boarding are carried inside the building. The brick boundary walls continue to form the external walls on the north and east sides.

Acknowledgment
The editors acknowledge the help of John Campbell of Terry Farrell and Company in the preparation of this article.

The school's accommodation is grouped in two distinct blocks. The first contains south-east-facing junior and infant teaching clusters, comprising eight classes with associated tutorial rooms, home bases and wet areas. The second houses shared facilities: music room, hall, kitchens (now largely redundant) and administrative offices. The entrance gives on to a central glazed conservatory between the blocks.

The layout is deep-plan. As much use as possible is made of natural light and ventilation and passive solar gain: 30 per cent of the external envelope is glazed, mostly concentrated on the south-east side to maximise winter solar gains. The roof is the dominant element. The eaves oversail the walls and glazing to provide protection from the high summer sun.

The pitched roofs are supported on a laminated timber structure on a 7.2 × 4.8 m grid. The paired rafters are supported on laminated columns at the perimeter and centre line. Main class areas are located south of the centre line with subsidiary and shared spaces to the north. Central areas of the deep plan are daylit through continuous ridge glazing.

The cross-section is designed to achieve high levels of through-ventilation in the summer. But the lack of a mechanical control system means that staff have to rely on cords—which break—or window poles to open the ridge lights. Consequently they tend not to be opened. This tendency, combined with the under-provision of opening lights in the perimeter glazing, means that summer stuffiness is sometimes a problem. Winter ventilation is through fanlights opening on to the conservatory.

Generally the building has worn remarkably well. The only significant failure has been the solar tinted polycarbonate sheet glazing in the conservatory which has suffered milking on the southern face. However:
● boundary walls and the brick storage blocks that project out from beneath the eaves have staining and moss growth due to the inadequacy of the brick coping detail
● stained softwood fascias—split to allow roof ventilation—have warped on the south and west sides where they are most exposed to the sun. The woodwork has only recently been restained for the first time although the manufacturer recommends recoating every three years to ensure adequate protection
● PVC gutters have sagged by as much as 12 mm between fixing brackets that are spaced too far apart. This encourages pooling which makes the problem worse
● mastic pointing around timber window frames on the west elevation has hardened and shrunk away from the brickwork, breaking the watertight seal.

Nearly all of these items could be solved by routine maintenance. ■

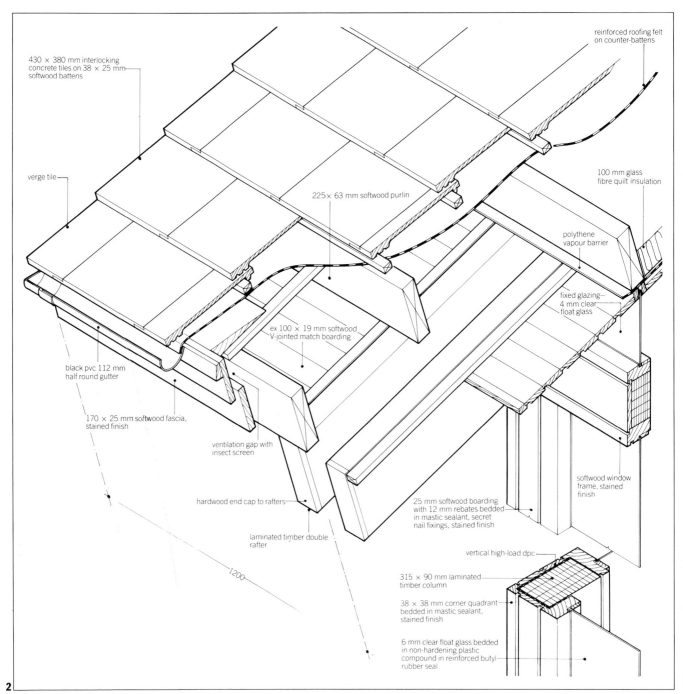

430 × 380 mm interlocking concrete tiles on 38 × 25 mm softwood battens

verge tile

reinforced roofing felt on counter-battens

100 mm glass fibre quilt insulation

225 × 63 mm softwood purlin

polythene vapour barrier

fixed glazing— 4 mm clear float glass

ex 100 × 19 mm softwood V-jointed match boarding

black pvc 112 mm half round gutter

170 × 25 mm softwood fascia, stained finish

ventilation gap with insect screen

hardwood end cap to rafters

softwood window frame, stained finish

25 mm softwood boarding with 12 mm rebates bedded in mastic sealant, secret nail fixings, stained finish

laminated timber double rafter

1200

vertical high-load dpc

315 × 90 mm laminated timber column

38 × 38 mm corner quadrant bedded in mastic sealant, stained finish

6 mm clear float glass bedded in non-hardening plastic compound in reinforced butyl rubber seal

2

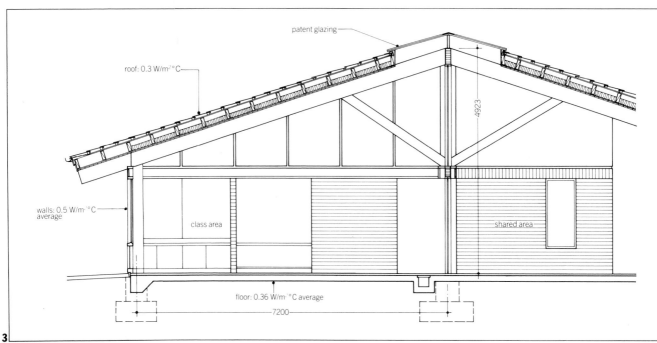

patent glazing

roof: 0.3 W/m²°C

4923

walls: 0.5 W/m²°C average

class area

shared area

floor: 0.36 W/m²°C average

7200

3

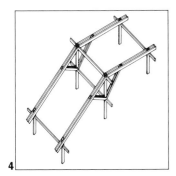

4

5

2 Eaves isometric at the corner of the classroom block.
3 Section through a typical classroom.
4 Diagram of teaching-block timber frame structure.
5 Boundary walls have suffered staining and moss growth. The gutter is too small for such a large expanse of roof: overloading has caused sagging between fixing brackets.
6 Detail sections at eaves and ground level through a typical classroom.

Credits
location Dungells Lane, Yateley, Hampshire
client Hampshire County Council
architect Hampshire County Architects Department
county architect Colin Stansfield Smith
directing architect H. B. Eaton
job architect Mervyn Perkins
quantity surveyor Langdon & Every
mechanical and electrical engineer Hampshire County Council
structural engineer Anthony Hunt Associates
main contractor H. N. Edwards & Partners
glulam timber frame Structural Timbers
roof patent glazing Ruberoid Contracts
conservatory glazing A. & T. Pritchard
sandlime bricks Ryarsh Brick Company
concrete blocks Arc Conbloc
concrete roof tiles Redland Tiles

Photo credit
Photographs by Charlotte Wood

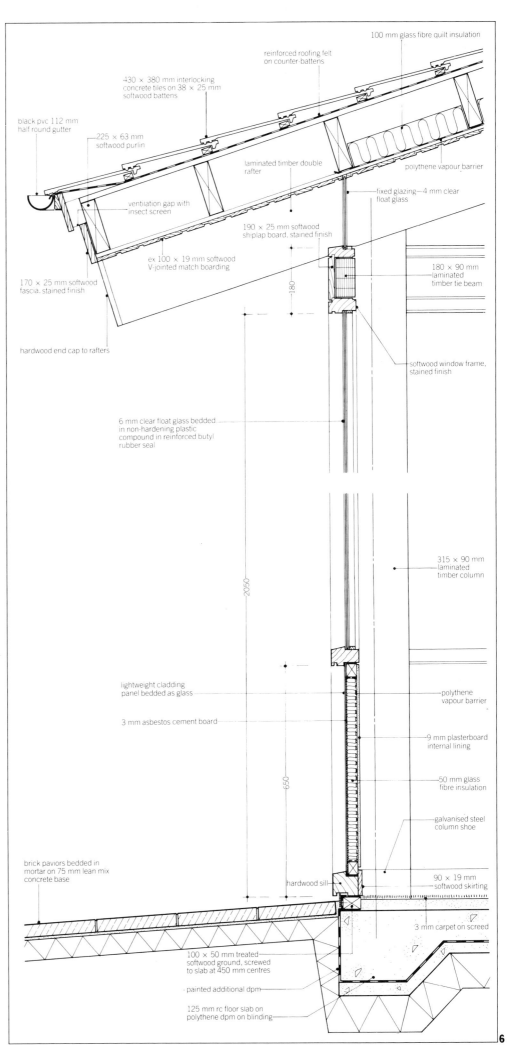

100 mm glass fibre quilt insulation
reinforced roofing felt on counter-battens
430 × 380 mm interlocking concrete tiles on 38 × 25 mm softwood battens
black pvc 112 mm half round gutter
225 × 63 mm softwood purlin
laminated timber double rafter
polythene vapour barrier
ventilation gap with insect screen
fixed glazing—4 mm clear float glass
190 × 25 mm softwood shiplap board. stained finish
ex 100 × 19 mm softwood V-jointed match boarding
180 × 90 mm laminated timber tie beam
170 × 25 mm softwood fascia. stained finish
hardwood end cap to rafters
softwood window frame, stained finish
6 mm clear float glass bedded in non-hardening plastic compound in reinforced butyl rubber seal
315 × 90 mm laminated timber column
lightweight cladding panel bedded as glass
polythene vapour barrier
3 mm asbestos cement board
9 mm plasterboard internal lining
50 mm glass fibre insulation
galvanised steel column shoe
brick paviors bedded in mortar on 75 mm lean mix concrete base
hardwood sill
90 × 19 mm softwood skirting
3 mm carpet on screed
100 × 50 mm treated softwood ground, screwed to slab at 450 mm centres
painted additional dpm
125 mm rc floor slab on polythene dpm on blinding

6

EXTERNAL WALLS AND ROOF
PRESS FACILITY
Denton Scott Associates

The walls and roof of the Jimmy Brown Centre at Silverstone are clad in PVF2-coated profiled metal sheet. Continuous inclined glazing allows uninterrupted views of the circuit.

1 At the front and gable ends, the roof oversails the walls, supported on V-props and anchored by tensioned cables.

Acknowledgment
The editors acknowledge the help of John Campbell of Terry Farrell and Company in the preparation of this article.

Silverstone Racing Circuit's new press facility is constructed above the existing pits. The superstructure is steel-framed and built off a platform supported on the underpinned and extended pits columns. The building is entered from the paddock through a new reception area on the site of the first pit.

The front elevation has a full-length, 3 m high, inclined double-glazed screen that allows journalists and cameramen unimpeded views of the circuit. At the eastern end, a winner's balcony cantilevers out over the pit lane.

The press room is a single, hangar-like multi-functional space, capable of subdivision by movable screens. Its roof curves downward towards the back of the plan where support functions (facsimile, telephone rooms and photo labs) are located. This allows rain-water to be channelled to the paddock elevation, leaving the front free of downpipes.

A break in the roof line articulates the junction between the press room and cellular ancillary rooms and allows a ventilation zone for the air-handling plant. At the front and gable ends, the roof oversails the walls. The overhang is supported from below by V-props and is anchored to the floor platform by tensioned cables to resist wind uplift.

Internally, tubular steel props, connected to the roof truss bottom booms, give mid-point support to the steel angle section purlins, thereby reducing their span and structural depth and giving them lateral stiffness. The

trusses connect to CHS columns anchored to the floor platform structure. All these components are expressed and finished with white silicone enamel.

Further detailed considerations include:
● walls and roof are clad with 0.65 mm thick PVF2-coated profiled metal sheet. Internally, above the press hall, the 0.5 mm thick polyester-coated roof lining sheet is perforated for acoustic performance. Externally, at roof overhangs, the lining sheet is 0.65 mm thick, unperforated, with a white acrylic coating
● walls below truss level are: 90 mm concrete facing block inner leaf; vapour barrier; 10 mm cavity; 100 mm semi-rigid slab insulation between metal studs; breather membrane; clad as above
● walls at truss level are: 125 mm thick woodwool slabs factory prescreeded on both faces cut to follow the roof profile; breather paper; clad as above
● exposed structural steelwork above the pits is coated with Nullifire System 600, finished in dark grey, to give half-hour fire resistance, and weather-protected with two additional coats of dark grey Topseal at the beam ends.

The inclined glazed screen is glazed with toughened safety glass; 6 mm thick at the outer leaf, 10 mm thick at the inner leaf. A tubular steel guard-rail provides an additional barrier between over-enthusiastic journalists and the track below. ■

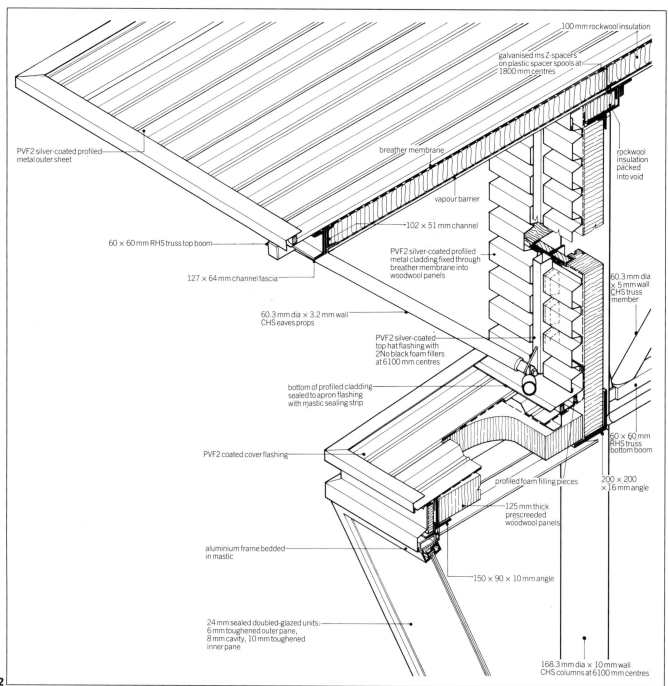

100 mm rockwool insulation

galvanised ms Z-spacers on plastic spacer spools at 1800 mm centres

rockwool insulation packed into void

breather membrane

PVF2 silver-coated profiled metal outer sheet

vapour barrier

102 × 51 mm channel

60 × 60 mm RHS truss top boom

PVF2 silver-coated profiled metal cladding fixed through breather membrane into woodwool panels

60.3 mm dia × 5 mm wall CHS truss member

127 × 64 mm channel fascia

60.3 mm dia × 3.2 mm wall CHS eaves props

PVF2 silver-coated top hat flashing with 2No black foam fillers at 6100 mm centres

bottom of profiled cladding sealed to apron flashing with mastic sealing strip

60 × 60 mm RHS truss bottom boom

200 × 200 × 16 mm angle

PVF2 coated cover flashing

profiled foam filling pieces

125 mm thick prescreeded woodwool panels

aluminium frame bedded in mastic

150 × 90 × 10 mm angle

24 mm sealed doubled-glazed units: 6 mm toughened outer pane, 8 mm cavity, 10 mm toughened inner pane

168.3 mm dia × 10 mm wall CHS columns at 6100 mm centres

2

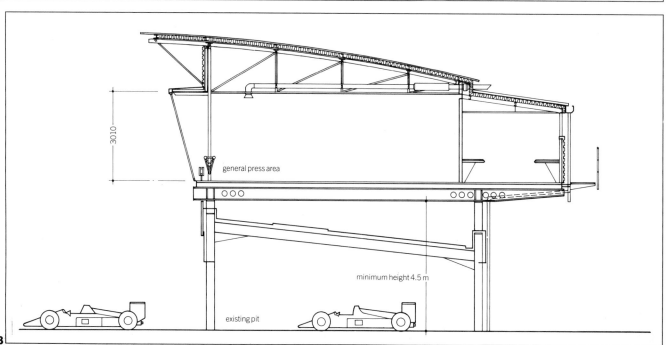

3010

general press area

minimum height 4.5 m

existing pit

3

4

2 Cut-away isometric of the wall cladding and roof assembly at the eaves.
3 Cross-section through the press hall. The new building is built off of a steel-framed platform above the existing pits.
4 Rear elevation detail.
5 Section through the press room roof and inclined glazed screen.

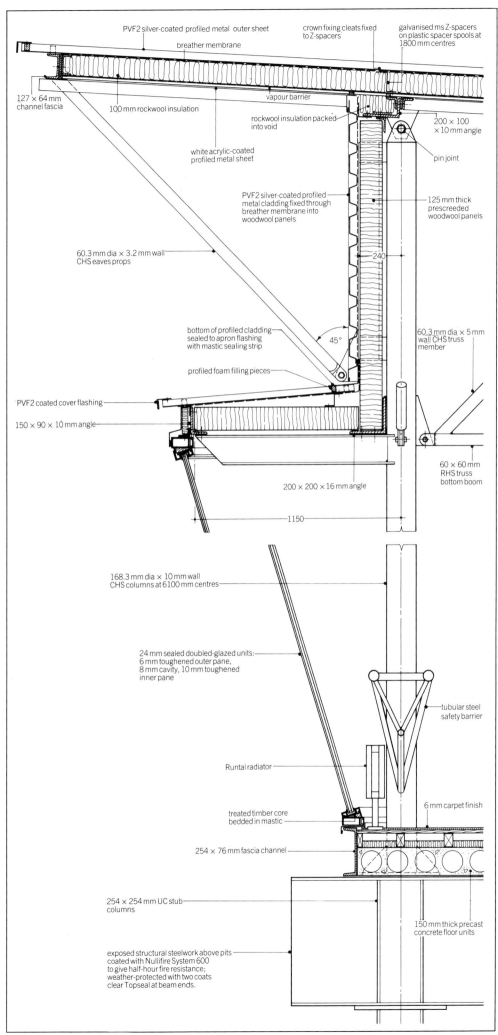

PVF2 silver-coated profiled metal outer sheet

breather membrane

crown fixing cleats fixed to Z-spacers

galvanised ms Z-spacers on plastic spacer spools at 1800 mm centres

vapour barrier

127 × 64 mm channel fascia

100 mm rockwool insulation

rockwool insulation packed into void

200 × 100 × 10 mm angle

pin joint

white acrylic-coated profiled metal sheet

PVF2 silver-coated profiled metal cladding fixed through breather membrane into woodwool panels

125 mm thick prescreeded woodwool panels

60.3 mm dia × 3.2 mm wall CHS eaves props

240

45°

60.3 mm dia × 5 mm wall CHS truss member

bottom of profiled cladding sealed to apron flashing with mastic sealing strip

profiled foam filling pieces

PVF2 coated cover flashing

150 × 90 × 10 mm angle

60 × 60 mm RHS truss bottom boom

200 × 200 × 16 mm angle

1150

168.3 mm dia × 10 mm wall CHS columns at 6100 mm centres

24 mm sealed doubled-glazed units: 6 mm toughened outer pane, 8 mm cavity, 10 mm toughened inner pane

tubular steel safety barrier

Runtal radiator

treated timber core bedded in mastic

6 mm carpet finish

254 × 76 mm fascia channel

254 × 254 mm UC stub columns

150 mm thick precast concrete floor units

exposed structural steelwork above pits coated with Nullifire System 600 to give half-hour fire resistance; weather-protected with two coats clear Topseal at beam ends.

5

Credits
client George Smith, development director, Silverstone Circuits
location Silverstone Circuit, Northamptonshire
architect Denton Scott Associates
design director Andrew Scott
project architect Adrian Morrow
assistant Chris Bannister
quantity surveyor and project manager Henry Cooper
structural engineer John Parkhouse Partnership
original structural concept Mark Whitby, Whitby and Bird
electrical consultant Barrie Wilde
mechanical services consultant A. C. Engineering Services
acoustic consultant Walker Beak Mason Partnership
structural steel frame Preform Engineering Co (Structural)
precast concrete floor units Richard Lees
fire protection Stuart Foster (Painting Contractors)
general builders' work Calverton Construction
roofing and cladding W. W. Roofing and Cladding
glazed wall and patent glazing Solaglas
screeding Neil A. Tedding Plastering
painting Gillies and Wilson Painters and Decorators
tubular steel safety barriers L. G. Kimber (Engineering)
suppliers: roofing and cladding sheets Plannja (UK), *concrete blocks* ARC Conbloc, *intumescent paint* Nullifire, *high build silicone enamel* Protection, *woodwool slabs* Torvale, *dritherm cavity insulation* Fibreglass, *rigging cables and turnbuckles* Sutch Lifting Equipment.

Photo credit
Photographs by Peter Cook.

EXTERNAL WALLS
RESIDENTIAL BUILDING
Elder & Cannon

Superficially similar elements of this corner turret are constructed in quite different ways. The lower cornice is stone and brick, while the upper cornices are lightweight GRC.

1 The lightweight, steel-framed part of the turret extends over two floors, with a lantern on top for the benefit of the penthouse flat.

Acknowledgment
The editors acknowledge the help of John Campbell of Terry Farrell and Company and Lionel Friedland of Pentarch in the preparation of this article.

This corner turret is the most prominent feature of an eight-storey residential block at Ingram Square, Glasgow. For the first six storeys the turret is a composite structure. The in-situ concrete slabs of the main structure are extended outwards and supported on a steel frame clad in brickwork. For the top two floors an independent steel structure is introduced in the form of a ring of circular section columns. These are extended upwards beyond the main roof line to form a lantern.

An interesting aspect of this construction is that superficially similar elements, such as the cornices at sixth-floor and roof levels, are constructed in quite different ways. The sixth floor forms the base of the circular steel structure. Here the concrete floor slab is extended into the turret and finished by a curved edge beam. As well as supporting the ring of steel columns, this edge beam provides a suitably solid base for a brick and reconstructed stone cornice.

The brickwork is supported on a galvanised steel angle bolted to the edge beam while the stone cornice is supported partly on the brickwork and partly on a concrete nib.

In contrast, the cornices at roof level and at the top of the lantern are made in glass-reinforced cement. Here there is no concrete slab to support brickwork or stone and a lighter cladding is required. The GRC mouldings are fixed to a timber frame by

means of coach screws with stainless steel washers and neoprene gaskets. The timber frame is in turn fixed to the steel structure.

At seventh-floor level, half-way up the steel-framed part of the turret, there is yet another solution to the floor/external wall junction. There is no projecting cornice at this level. Instead the timber-framed curtain-wall, made up from proprietary tilt-and-turn windows, passes over the floor slab, interrupted only by an insulated fibre cement (Glasal) panel set in the same plane as the glass.

The lower roof is lead-covered, while the lantern roof is covered in three-layer felt. The radial structure of these roofs is mainly timber with firrings sloping towards the perimeter to shed rain-water into aluminium ogee gutters.

The details raise a number of performance questions, especially in relation to the stone cornice at sixth-floor level:
● dpcs under the reconstructed stone are difficult to form around the curve. Small radial sections are overlapped and bonded together. The dpc is supported within the cavity by sections of stainless steel mesh. In theory, water can travel across the cavity on the underside of the horizontal dpc
● dirt washed off the top surface of the sill may cause streaking on the front face before reaching the drip on the underside
● the intumescent coating to the exposed steel columns provides one-hour fire protection and is formulated for external use. ■

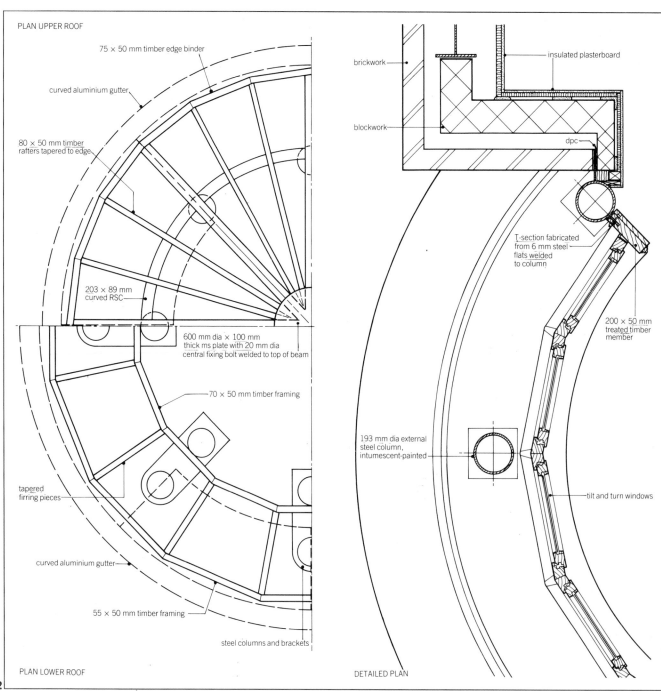

PLAN UPPER ROOF

75 × 50 mm timber edge binder

curved aluminium gutter

80 × 50 mm timber rafters tapered to edge

203 × 89 mm curved RSC

600 mm dia × 100 mm thick ms plate with 20 mm dia central fixing bolt welded to top of beam

70 × 50 mm timber framing

tapered firring pieces

curved aluminium gutter

55 × 50 mm timber framing

steel columns and brackets

PLAN LOWER ROOF

brickwork

insulated plasterboard

blockwork

dpc

T-section fabricated from 6 mm steel flats welded to column

200 × 50 mm treated timber member

193 mm dia external steel column, intumescent-painted

tilt and turn windows

DETAILED PLAN

2

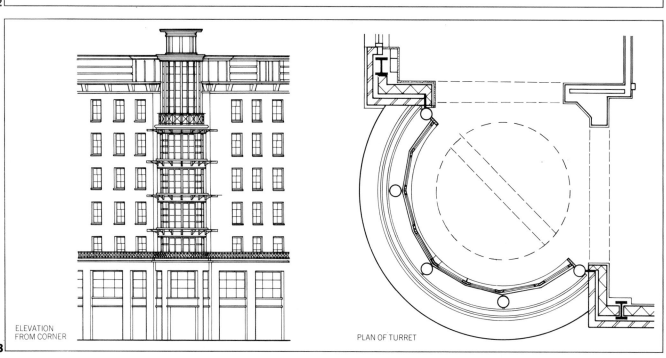

ELEVATION FROM CORNER

PLAN OF TURRET

3

4

5

2 Plans showing the roof framing and the junction with the brickwork cladding.
3 Elevation of complete corner turret and plan at sixth-floor level.
4 Inside the penthouse flat the turret becomes a dining-room alcove.
5 The turret is supported by a ring of exposed, circular section steel columns.
6 Detailed section. Compare the stone sill with the GRC cornice.

Credits
location Ingram Square, Glasgow
client Ingram Square Ltd (Kantel), Scottish Development Agency, Glasgow District Council
architect Elder & Cannon
quantity surveyor Tozer Gallagher and Partners
structural engineer Blyth and Blyth Partnership
main contractor Lawrence Construction
subcontractors: steel frame Bone Connell and Baxter
decorative metalwork Findlay Campbell
timber windows Hall and Tawse
render, partitions and roof Gypsum Construction

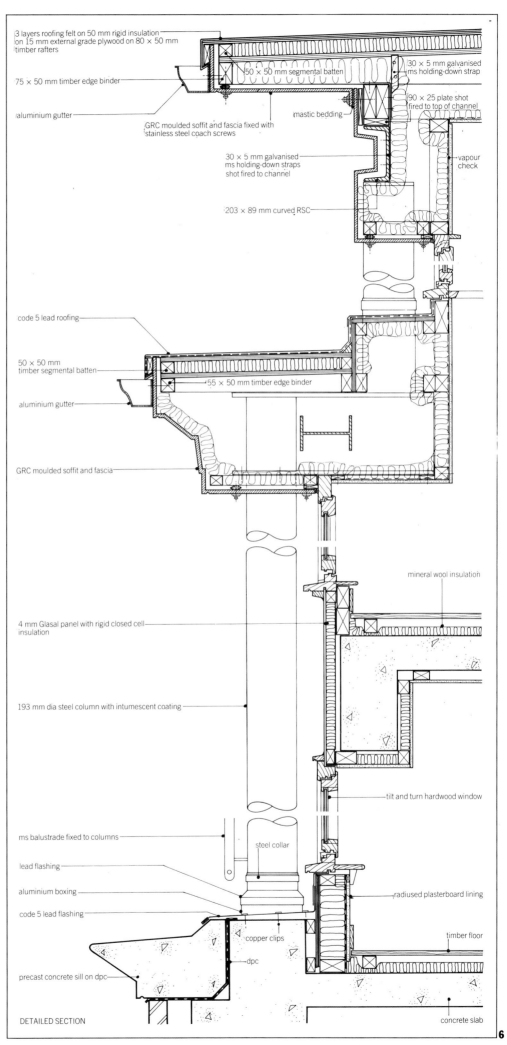

3 layers roofing felt on 50 mm rigid insulation on 15 mm external grade plywood on 80 × 50 mm timber rafters

75 × 50 mm timber edge binder

aluminium gutter

GRC moulded soffit and fascia fixed with stainless steel coach screws

50 × 50 mm segmental batten

mastic bedding

30 × 5 mm galvanised ms holding-down strap

90 × 25 plate shot fired to top of channel

vapour check

30 × 5 mm galvanised ms holding-down straps shot fired to channel

203 × 89 mm curved RSC

code 5 lead roofing

50 × 50 mm timber segmental batten

55 × 50 mm timber edge binder

aluminium gutter

GRC moulded soffit and fascia

mineral wool insulation

4 mm Glasal panel with rigid closed cell insulation

193 mm dia steel column with intumescent coating

tilt and turn hardwood window

ms balustrade fixed to columns

steel collar

lead flashing

aluminium boxing

radiused plasterboard lining

code 5 lead flashing

copper clips

timber floor

dpc

precast concrete sill on dpc

concrete slab

DETAILED SECTION

6

EXTERNAL WALLS AND ROOF
VISITORS' CENTRE
Van Heyningen and Haward

Clovelly Visitors' Centre is a steel-framed building with insulated rendered blockwork walls and a slate roof which echo the Devon vernacular.

1

1 View across country from the south-east. The building occupies a hilltop site above the village of Clovelly on the north Devon coast and spans the existing pathway from the car park to the village, controlling entry and providing facilities for visitors.

Acknowledgment
The editors acknowledge the help of John Campbell of Terry Farrell and Company and Lionel Friedland of Pentarch in the preparation of this article.

The visitors' centre is situated at the east end of the car park on a hill above the village to which it forms a gateway. The existing steeply sloping path (about 1:8) down to the village now runs through its main concourse and exhibition space. Visitors enter from the car park into a single-storey foyer and proceed down wide stairs into a double-height space and on out along the path to the village. Push-chairs and the disabled can turn off at right angles at the centre of the building and follow a ramp to the lower level.

The buildings situated on the hilltop above Clovelly, such as the coastguard cottages and the stables, are simple in form, but large and long, and so is the visitors' centre. Externally its materials are those of all the local buildings: slate roof and white-washed rendered walls.

Because of the need to construct the building during the six winter months when there are few visitors, the structure is a steel frame at 5 m centres; the flat-plate roof trusses are exposed and painted pale blue, but the columns supporting them are encased in blockwork and take the form of pilasters on the outside and inside of the building. Between the columns, the 190 mm blockwork walls are painted fairfaced on the inside, with a proprietary 50 mm insulation and 25 mm render system on the outside.

The cafeteria is carpeted and the ceiling is highly absorbent: this is a successful acoustic approach which aimed to make the space feel comfortable even when sparsely occupied.

Further detailed considerations include:
● the roof is covered with 500 × 250 mm slates on 38 × 25 m tantalised sw battens on roofing felt. The 150 × 50 mm tanalised sw rafters at 420 mm centres are fixed by means of 100 × 50 mm sw plates bolted to the 178 × 102 RSJ purlins. Thermal and acoustic insulation is provided by a 40 mm thick white self-finish metal-edged panel system with a ventilated cavity above
● balustrading to external terrace areas is of double-vacuum preservative-treated softwood, stained black. The balustrade posts are oversized to fit over a reinforcing 80 × 80 mm RHS post bolted to the tops of the columns at slab level on the structural grid lines. Intermediate posts fit over an RHS bolted, via a welded ms plate, to the top of the parapet wall
● a narrow hardwood-framed, double-glazed, clerestory window with opening lights runs all the way round the building at eaves level to mark the point where the steel structure becomes exposed, and to provide natural ventilation to all the spaces. The remaining windows are all off-the-peg square hardwood frames. Internally a band of 65 mm square ceramic tiles surrounds each window, concealing the 75 × 65 mm tanalised sw subframe, and providing a rare element of surface decoration. ∎

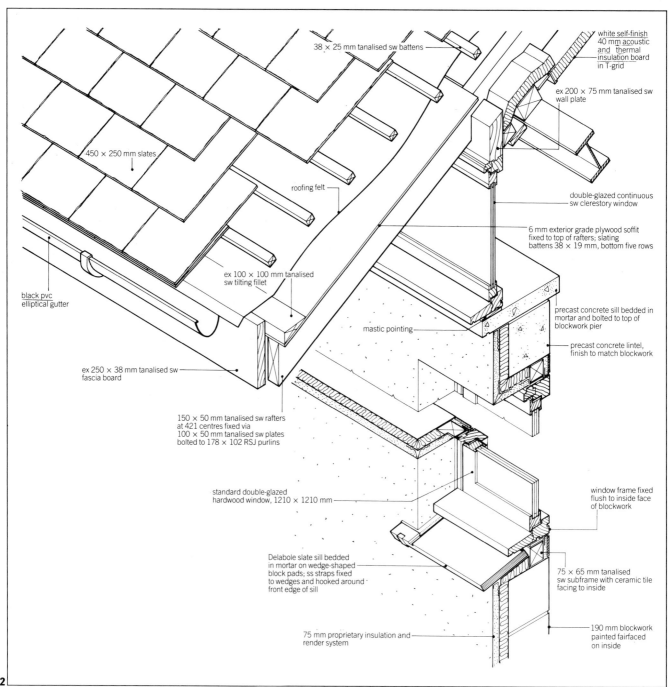

white self-finish 40 mm acoustic and thermal insulation board in T-grid

38 × 25 mm tanalised sw battens

ex 200 × 75 mm tanalised sw wall plate

double-glazed continuous sw clerestory window

450 × 250 mm slates

roofing felt

6 mm exterior grade plywood soffit fixed to top of rafters; slating battens 38 × 19 mm, bottom five rows

ex 100 × 100 mm tanalised sw tilting fillet

black pvc elliptical gutter

precast concrete sill bedded in mortar and bolted to top of blockwork pier

mastic pointing

precast concrete lintel, finish to match blockwork

ex 250 × 38 mm tanalised sw fascia board

150 × 50 mm tanalised sw rafters at 421 centres fixed via 100 × 50 mm tanalised sw plates bolted to 178 × 102 RSJ purlins

window frame fixed flush to inside face of blockwork

standard double-glazed hardwood window, 1210 × 1210 mm

Delabole slate sill bedded in mortar on wedge-shaped block pads; ss straps fixed to wedges and hooked around front edge of sill

75 × 65 mm tanalised sw subframe with ceramic tile facing to inside

190 mm blockwork painted fairfaced on inside

75 mm proprietary insulation and render system

2

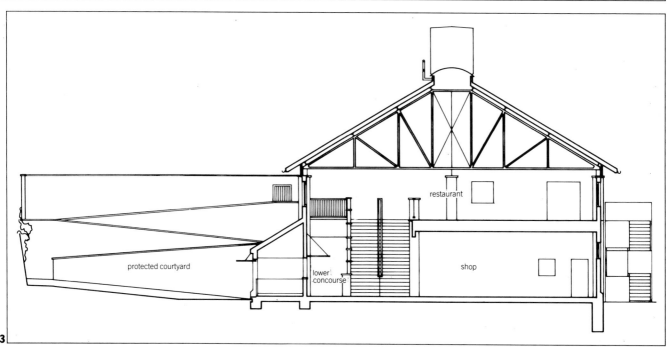

restaurant

protected courtyard

lower concourse

shop

3

2 Isometric detail of the eaves assembly and window at upper level. The window sills are of Dalebole slate with drainage channels cut in each end to prevent water soaking the rendered reveals.
3 Section through the building.
4 The south elevation adjacent to the car park. The building is sited at right angles to the sloping ground, changing from single-storey at the landward car park end to two storeys at the seaward end.
5 Composite section through the external envelope showing typical eaves, upper- and lower-level window and plinth details. The plinth detail is a potential weak point. Rain-water soaking through the 25 mm render could collect on top of the dpc and run back to pool on top of the dpm. A stepped dpc/dpm junction would prevent this.

Credits
location Clovelly, Devon
client Clovelly Estate Company
architect van Heyningen and Haward Architects
partner in charge Birkin Haward
job architect Robin Mallalieu
assistant James Philipps
structural engineer Price & Myers
quantity surveyor Hanscomb Partnership
mechanical engineer Pearce & Associates
main contractor Pearce Construction (Barnstaple)
subcontractors: rooflights Metrobuild Products, *electrical* P. F. Friend & Son, *barrier rails* Tensator, *heaters* Heatrae Industrial, *windows and doors* Sarek Joinery, *doors* Crosby Doors, *steelwork* E. D. Hughes Engineers, *slate roof* Burlington Slate.
suppliers: vent louvres Greenwood Airvac, *precast concrete* Dabro, *bricks* Steetley, *mortar additive* Tilcon, *hardwood window* Sarek Joinery *heaters* Heatrae, *aluminium windows* Glostal, *floor tiles* Dennis Ruabon.

Photo credit
Photographs by Heini Schneebli.

5

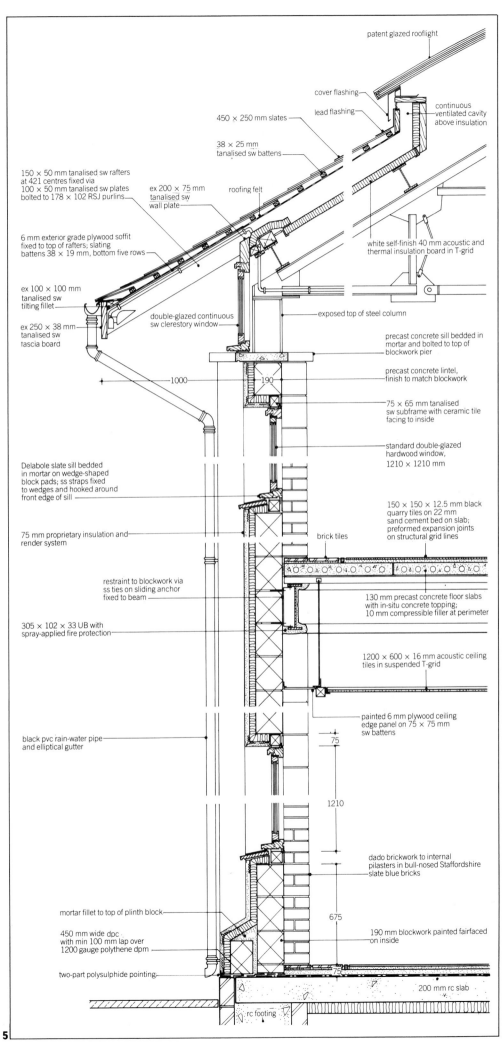

patent glazed rooflight

cover flashing

lead flashing

continuous ventilated cavity above insulation

450 × 250 mm slates

38 × 25 mm tanalised sw battens

150 × 50 mm tanalised sw rafters at 421 centres fixed via 100 × 50 mm tanalised sw plates bolted to 178 × 102 RSJ purlins

ex 200 × 75 mm tanalised sw wall plate

roofing felt

white self-finish 40 mm acoustic and thermal insulation board in T-grid

6 mm exterior grade plywood soffit fixed to top of rafters; slating battens 38 × 19 mm, bottom five rows

ex 100 × 100 mm tanalised sw tilting fillet

double-glazed continuous sw clerestory window

exposed top of steel column

ex 250 × 38 mm tanalised sw fascia board

precast concrete sill bedded in mortar and bolted to top of blockwork pier

precast concrete lintel, finish to match blockwork

75 × 65 mm tanalised sw subframe with ceramic tile facing to inside

1000

190

standard double-glazed hardwood window, 1210 × 1210 mm

Delabole slate sill bedded in mortar on wedge-shaped block pads; ss straps fixed to wedges and hooked around front edge of sill

150 × 150 × 12.5 mm black quarry tiles on 22 mm sand cement bed on slab; preformed expansion joints on structural grid lines

brick tiles

75 mm proprietary insulation and render system

restraint to blockwork via ss ties on sliding anchor fixed to beam

130 mm precast concrete floor slabs with in-situ concrete topping; 10 mm compressible filler at perimeter

305 × 102 × 33 UB with spray-applied fire protection

1200 × 600 × 16 mm acoustic ceiling tiles in suspended T-grid

painted 6 mm plywood ceiling edge panel on 75 × 75 mm sw battens

black pvc rain-water pipe and elliptical gutter

75

1210

dado brickwork to internal pilasters in bull-nosed Staffordshire slate blue bricks

675

mortar fillet to top of plinth block

450 mm wide dpc with min 100 mm lap over 1200 gauge polythene dpm

190 mm blockwork painted fairfaced on inside

two-part polysulphide pointing

75

200 mm rc slab

rc footing

EXTERNAL WALLS AND ROOF
POOL HOUSE
Tim Ronalds Architects

This small pool house for a private client in Hampstead Garden Suburb has timber-framed walls clad in cedar boarding and a standing-seam copper roof.

1

1 The pool house viewed from the south-east.

The pool house is built beside an existing outdoor swimming-pool in the garden of a house in Hampstead Garden Suburb. The pool house provides simple changing facilities and a store-room, but beyond that is intended to make the pool-side more habitable and encourage outdoor life. The idea was to make the building a simple composition of sculptural elements which would spatially engage the pool and garden.

Three main elements compose the building: a white-painted rendered perimeter wall, a horizontally banded timber wall, and a cantilevering timber pergola. They are bound together by a slender steel beam. The building is a simple assembly of these elements.

The timber wall is clad with wide western red cedar boards fixed to studwork by means of tongued and grooved mahogany battens which are screwed back to the softwood studding and the holes pelleted. The cedar is untreated and the horizontal banded appearance will become more emphasised as the cedar weathers to a silver-grey.

The slender steel beam, a 102 × 102 mm RSJ, is supported on the wall and a paired tubular steel column. Turned brass column caps enrich the junction of beam and column. The steel is treated with epoxy paint and finished in micaceous iron oxide.

The pergola, constructed of 144 × 69 mm Douglas fir, is tied down to the boundary wall and cantilevers over the steel beam to the edge of the swimming-pool. The Douglas fir is double-vacuum preservative-treated and sealed to maintain its colour. The pergola supports the sandwich construction ventilated plywood roof deck over the changing room which is finished with standing-seam copper roofing. A purpose-made flat rooflight on the roof top-lights the rear wall of the changing room. Condensation on the underside of the glass is avoided by incorporating ventilation slots in the timber frame.

Inside the changing room the external pattern of banded cedar boarding is continued but with flush boards. The internal elements, cupboards, bench and shower are all made in cedar, and in contrast to the outside the warm golden colour will remain unweathered. The building inside has the feel and smell of a cigar box. The shower is a three-quarter cylinder of edge-glued vertical t & g cedar boards and drains to a floor gulley concealed below the cedar duckboards. The 'lights' are the small 'windows' set between bands of boarding which contain a lamp set behind a piece of medicine-bottle-blue glass. Outside, the table top is a 40 mm slab of site-cast black concrete which incorporates a small sink.

There are very few manufactured products visible in the building. Those that are unavoidable are concealed. The qualities of the materials, forms and space are not disrupted and the tiny building has unexpected sculptural force. ∎

Acknowledgment
The editors acknowledge the help of John Campbell of Terry Farrell and Company and Lionel Friedland of Pentarch in the preparation of this article.

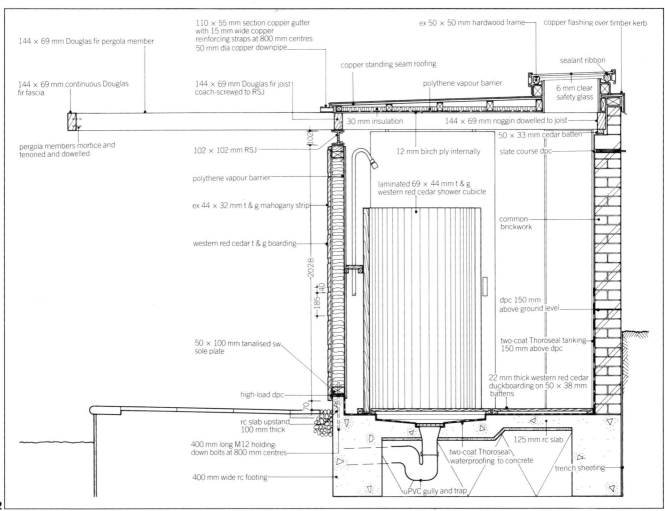

144 × 69 mm Douglas fir pergola member

144 × 69 mm continuous Douglas fir fascia

pergola members mortice and tenoned and dowelled

110 × 55 mm section copper gutter with 15 mm wide copper reinforcing straps at 800 mm centres 50 mm dia copper downpipe

144 × 69 mm Douglas fir joist coach-screwed to RSJ

102 × 102 mm RSJ

polythene vapour barrier

ex 44 × 32 mm t & g mahogany strip

western red cedar t & g boarding

50 × 100 mm tanalised sw sole plate

high-load dpc

rc slab upstand 100 mm thick

400 mm long M12 holding-down bolts at 800 mm centres

400 mm wide rc footing

ex 50 × 50 mm hardwood frame

copper standing seam roofing

polythene vapour barrier

30 mm insulation

12 mm birch ply internally

laminated 69 × 44 mm t & g western red cedar shower cubicle

copper flashing over timber kerb

sealant ribbon

6 mm clear safety glass

144 × 69 mm noggin dowelled to joist

50 × 33 mm cedar batten

slate course dpc

common brickwork

dpc 150 mm above ground level

two-coat Thoroseal tanking 150 mm above dpc

22 mm thick western red cedar duckboarding on 50 × 38 mm battens

125 mm rc slab

two-coat Thoroseal waterproofing to concrete

trench sheeting

uPVC gully and trap

2

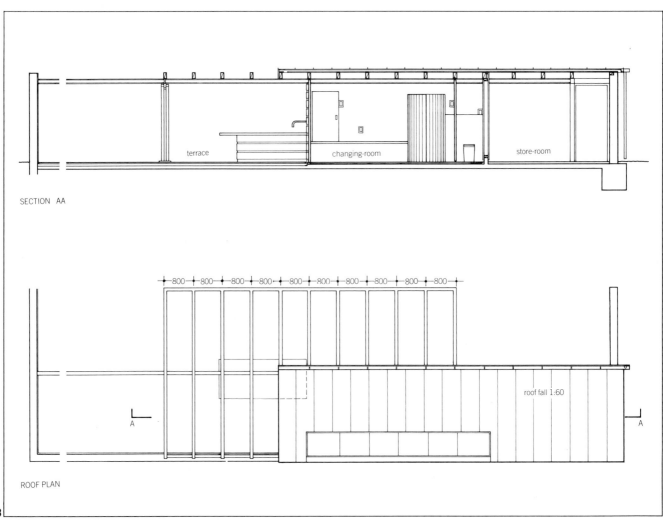

terrace

changing-room

store-room

SECTION AA

800 800 800 800 800 800 800 800 800 800

roof fall 1:60

A

A

ROOF PLAN

3

4

2 Section through the changing room and shower cubicle.
3 Long section AA and roof plan.
4 Detail of the cedar and mahogany banded boarding. The cedar will eventually fade to silver-grey; the mahogany is sealed to retain its colour.
5 Isometric details of the frame and cladding at an external corner. The cedar boards are fixed by means of t & g mahogany strips; the lowest cedar board is screwed to the studs and pelleted. The boards are mitred at the corner to avoid exposing the end grain.

copper standing seam roofing

110 × 55 mm section copper gutter with 15 mm wide copper reinforcing straps at 800 mm centres
50 mm dia copper downpipe

felt underlay

18 mm WBP sheathing

144 × 69 mm Douglas fir joist coach-screwed to RSJ

polythene vapour barrier

two-part polysulphide seal

30 mm insulation

102 × 102 mm RSJ

12 mm birch-faced ply pinned and glued

polythene vapour barrier

ventilation slot with insect screen

ex 45 × 12 mm mahogany t&g internal strip finished flush

ex 95 × 12 mm western red cedar t & g internal boarding

coloured glass infill

100 mm glass-fibre quilt

100 × 50 mm sw studs at 400m centres

ex 195 × 25 mm western red cedar t & g external boarding

board butt joints grooved and loose-tongued on stud centres

cedar boards mitred at corners

polished black concrete worktop

ex 50 × 23 mm mahogany t & g external strip screwed to studs and pelleted

12 mm birch ply internally

washed pebbles drainage slot

50 × 100 mm tanalised sw sole plate

high-load dpc

rc slab upstand 100 mm thick

125 mm rc slab

5

Credits
location Hampstead Garden Suburb, London NW11
architect Tim Ronalds Architects: Tim Ronalds assisted by Kalliope Kontozoglou, Gerard MacCreanor
structural engineer Trigram Partnership: Rene Wiesner
contractor T. S. Bourton
specialist metalwork Dowling Design & Development

Photo credit
Photographs by Charlotte Wood

EXTERNAL WALLS AND ROOF
OFFICES
YRM Partnership

The metal cladding system for these offices, now 12 years old, has maintained its crisp appearance.

1

1 Part of the east elevation to YRM's offices looking towards Britton Street. The glazing reflects not only the older surrounding buildings but also the block of flats which is part of the development.

The YRM Partnership moved into its new building in 1977. When the practice found the site in 1971 it was already being developed as a warehouse, and the foundations were at a sufficiently advanced stage that it made sense for YRM to build literally on top of them. It was this that encouraged YRM to use a steel frame (with precast floors) and a relatively lightweight pressed aluminium cladding.

The offices form a neat, elegant three-storey glazed box with a two-storey brick podium below, which reaches into the awkward corners on the site. Having reused one of the original (but dismantled) Classical facades for the associated development of flats in Britton Street—which is linked to the new building by the podium—YRM was free to design the three storeys to the pavilion above the podium in the precisely engineered style characteristic of the practice's work.

The aluminium cladding was carefully detailed not only at panel-to-panel and panel-to-glazing junctions, but also at all the corners and around the columns. As a result little staining is evident—although the panels, primed, undercoated and painted with two coats of Long Oil Soya Alkyd Dull Gloss Paint (roller-applied to reduce the 'shininess') require repainting every five years or so, and have been repainted within the last two years.

The use of a factory-applied baked powder finish (such as Syntha Pulvin) was considered but at the time these finishes were less well proven, and in order to minimise site work each large bay of panels was fabricated in two parts at the works, a process which would not have easily accommodated prefinished panels. There is therefore a relatively high maintenance element in regular repainting. But the careful detailing, ensuring for instance that no mastic can be seen externally, means that this is a straightforward operation.

Whenever the panels are repainted, the galvanised grilles around the perimeter at the base of the building are also pressure-cleaned—this is necessary to remove the staining on them. These were an 'off-the-shelf' component which seemed suitable, although in retrospect a more robust purpose-designed grille might have been preferable.

The neoprene and internal grade polysulphide seals to several of the double-glazed panels appear now to have failed, resulting in condensation appearing inside the units, but this is not unexpected in panels of this age, and the panels will not be difficult to replace when necessary.

The roof of this building was treated as a fifth elevation, expressing the 1.8 m grid, YRM having skilfully managed to locate elsewhere the items that so often clutter up roofs. Possibly partly as a result of this there have been no problems at all with the built-up felt roof. ∎

Acknowledgment
The editors acknowledge the help of Alan Brookes of Alan Brookes Associates in the preparation of this article.

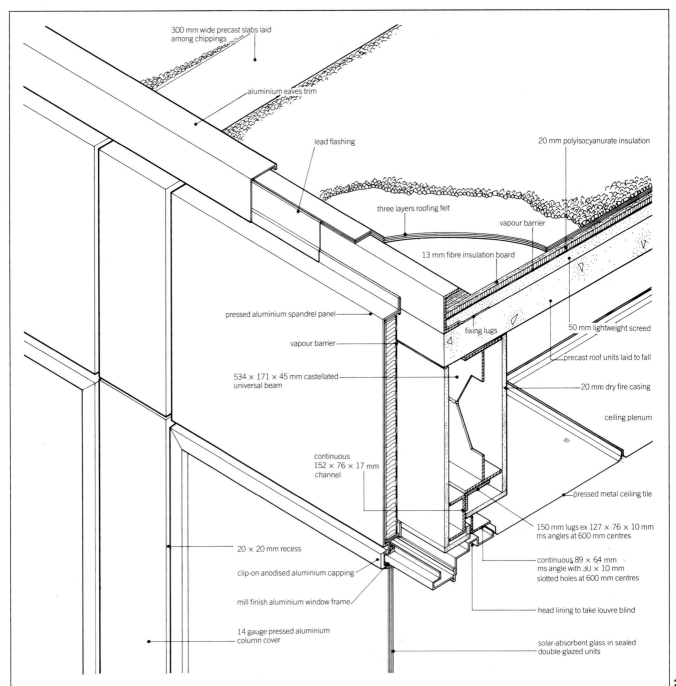

300 mm wide precast slabs laid among chippings

aluminium eaves trim

lead flashing

20 mm polyisocyanurate insulation

three layers roofing felt

vapour barrier

13 mm fibre insulation board

pressed aluminium spandrel panel

vapour barrier

534 × 171 × 45 mm castellated universal beam

fixing lugs

50 mm lightweight screed

precast roof units laid to fall

20 mm dry fire casing

ceiling plenum

continuous 152 × 76 × 17 mm channel

pressed metal ceiling tile

150 mm lugs ex 127 × 76 × 10 mm ms angles at 600 mm centres

20 × 20 mm recess

clip-on anodised aluminium capping

mill finish aluminium window frame

14 gauge pressed aluminium column cover

continuous 89 × 64 mm ms angle with 30 × 10 mm slotted holes at 600 mm centres

head lining to take louvre blind

solar-absorbent glass in sealed double-glazed units

2

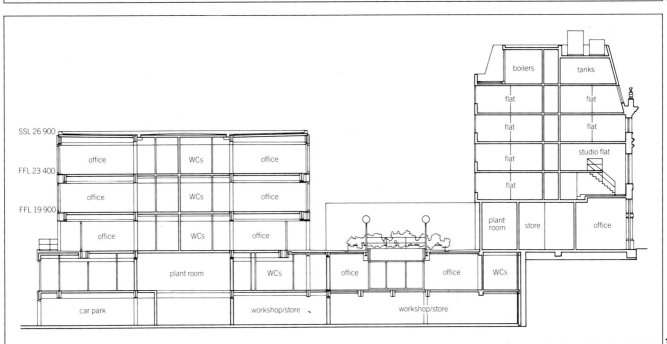

SSL 26 900

FFL 23 400

FFL 19 900

boilers | tanks

flat | flat

flat | flat

flat | studio flat

flat

office | WCs | office

office | WCs | office

office | WCs | office

plant room | store | office

plant room | WCs | office | office | WCs

car park | workshop/store | workshop/store

3

4

2 Cut-away isometric showing the cladding and roof construction.
3 Section through the development with the offices to the left, and, to the right, the residential building behind the reconstructed Classical facade to Britton Street.
4 Close-up of the south-east corner. The column cladding is articulated without interrupting the clean lines of the cladding system. The lines of the column cladding are continued across the roof with 300 mm wide precast concrete slabs, forming a fifth elevation.
5 Vertical section through the office pavilion and the roof of the podium below.

Credits
location 24 Britton Street, London EC1
client Amalgamated Investment Property Company
architect YRM Partnership Ltd (formerly Yorke Rosenberg Mardall) in association with Fitzroy Robinson & Partners
quantity surveyor Kinsler and Partners
structural engineer White Young and Partners
contractor Walter Lawrence & Sons Ltd

Photo credits
No 1 by Richard Turpin; No 4 by Heini Schneebeli.

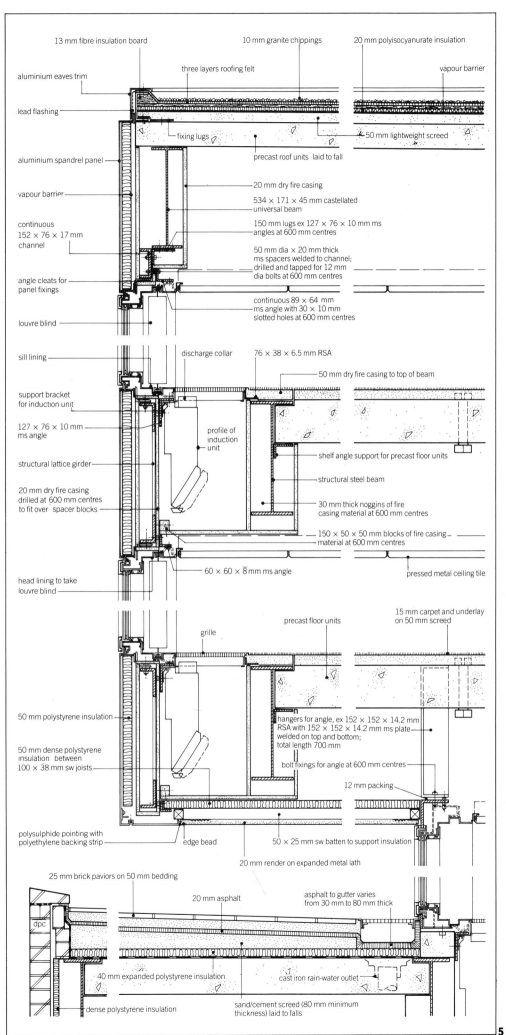

13 mm fibre insulation board
aluminium eaves trim
lead flashing
aluminium spandrel panel
vapour barrier
continuous 152 × 76 × 17 mm channel
angle cleats for panel fixings
louvre blind

10 mm granite chippings
three layers roofing felt
fixing lugs
precast roof units laid to fall

20 mm polyisocyanurate insulation
vapour barrier
50 mm lightweight screed

20 mm dry fire casing
534 × 171 × 45 mm castellated universal beam
150 mm lugs ex 127 × 76 × 10 mm ms angles at 600 mm centres
50 mm dia × 20 mm thick ms spacers welded to channel; drilled and tapped for 12 mm dia bolts at 600 mm centres
continuous 89 × 64 mm ms angle with 30 × 10 mm slotted holes at 600 mm centres

sill lining
support bracket for induction unit
127 × 76 × 10 mm ms angle
structural lattice girder
20 mm dry fire casing drilled at 600 mm centres to fit over spacer blocks
head lining to take louvre blind

discharge collar
profile of induction unit

76 × 38 × 6.5 mm RSA
50 mm dry fire casing to top of beam
shelf angle support for precast floor units
structural steel beam
30 mm thick noggins of fire casing material at 600 mm centres
150 × 50 × 50 mm blocks of fire casing material at 600 mm centres
60 × 60 × 8 mm ms angle
pressed metal ceiling tile

grille
precast floor units
15 mm carpet and underlay on 50 mm screed

50 mm polystyrene insulation
50 mm dense polystyrene insulation between 100 × 38 mm sw joists
polysulphide pointing with polyethylene backing strip
edge bead
50 × 25 mm sw batten to support insulation
20 mm render on expanded metal lath

hangers for angle, ex 152 × 152 × 14.2 mm RSA with 152 × 152 × 14.2 mm ms plate welded on top and bottom; total length 700 mm
bolt fixings for angle at 600 mm centres
12 mm packing

25 mm brick paviors on 50 mm bedding
dpc
40 mm expanded polystyrene insulation
dense polystyrene insulation

20 mm asphalt
asphalt to gutter varies from 30 mm to 80 mm thick
cast iron rain-water outlet
sand/cement screed (80 mm minimum thickness) laid to falls

EXTERNAL WALLS AND ROOF
OFFICES
Foster Associates

Foster Associates' 'temporary' office building for IBM, completed in 1972, has proved more lasting than many 'permanent' buildings.

1

1 The exact location of the part of the building shown in this photograph can be established only by reference to the reflections in the glass and the interior furnishing. The cladding continues around the building uninterrupted except by the doors.

Foster Associates' original brief for this building in 1970 was to provide low-budget offices of 'high architectural and environmental standards' with a life-span of up to 10 years.

The client had planned to use a single-storey prefabricated timber building system, and it was only due to Foster Associates' thorough analysis of the brief that such a radically different building form emerged.

In spite of its deceptively simple appearance and temporary nature, this is not a 'loose-fit' building. Its success—and it has now been refurbished to ensure a life-span of at least 25 years—is due to its being carefully tailored to meet very particular requirements.

The superstructure, which sits on a concrete raft, is formed from hollow 125 mm square steel columns which support a grid of steel lattice beams on a 7.315 m grid.

The glazing system, using imported American 'T' wall components to retain approximately 3.8 × 1.8 m panes of 9 mm bronze solar-absorbent glass, has lasted well and is a forerunner of British gasketed glazing systems such as Astrawall.

The weakest point in the building, apart from the built-up felt roof itself, was the junction of the roof and the walls. The single-glazed walls, although readily maintainable internally and externally, have no added insulation, but the original felt roofing sat on insulated ribbed steel decking,

and the junction of the two was covered by a plastic protected mild steel coping section bedded on mastic, and screwed back to the structure and the aluminium head section.

Cold bridging was therefore seen as being a potential problem here; but that problem did not materialise, either in the coping or the walling, at least partly because this is a largely open-plan building of a simple cuboid shape, which is totally air-conditioned. The layout of the building is also carefully planned so that nobody has to work next to the outside wall where there are extremes of heat and cold. Users find this a comfortable building.

When the roof covering had to be replaced in 1985, the coping detail was also renewed, having been redesigned to eliminate the mastic, but still carefully maintaining the simple edge along the top of the building.

The 300 mm raised floor in the computer room was one of the first in this country, but elsewhere service distribution was from within the ceiling void, all the service outlets being clustered around the bases of columns. This has now been expanded, although at the cost of flexibility of layout, with additional ducts running down the columns and linked to fixed desktop-level busbar trunking.

To meet the client's changing requirements, the internal layout has been altered, largely to accommodate a multiplication of computing power, but the basic function and character of the buildings are as originally intended. ∎

Acknowledgment
The editors acknowledge the help of John Pringle of Michael Hopkins and Partners in the preparation of this article.

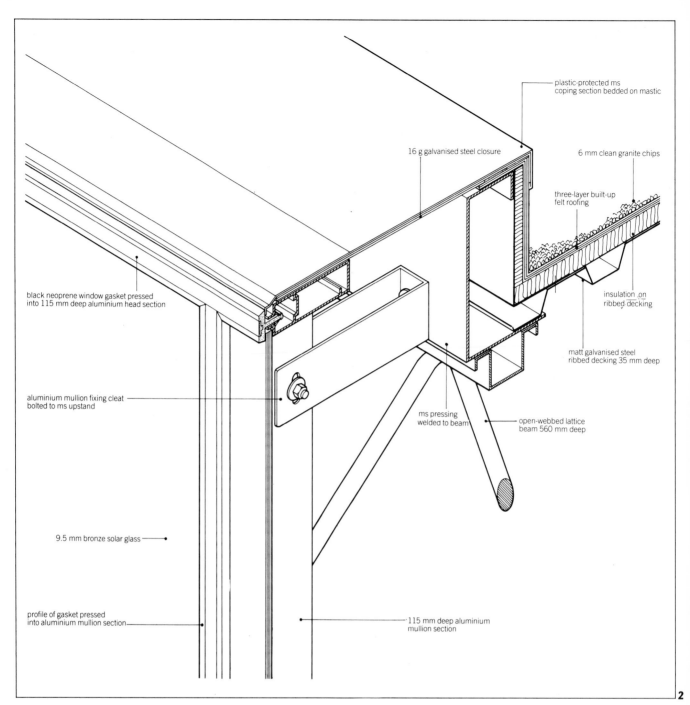

plastic-protected ms
coping section bedded on mastic

16 g galvanised steel closure

6 mm clean granite chips

three-layer built-up
felt roofing

black neoprene window gasket pressed
into 115 mm deep aluminium head section

insulation on
ribbed decking

aluminium mullion fixing cleat
bolted to ms upstand

matt galvanised steel
ribbed decking 35 mm deep

ms pressing
welded to beam

open-webbed lattice
beam 560 mm deep

9.5 mm bronze solar glass

profile of gasket pressed
into aluminium mullion section

115 mm deep aluminium
mullion section

2

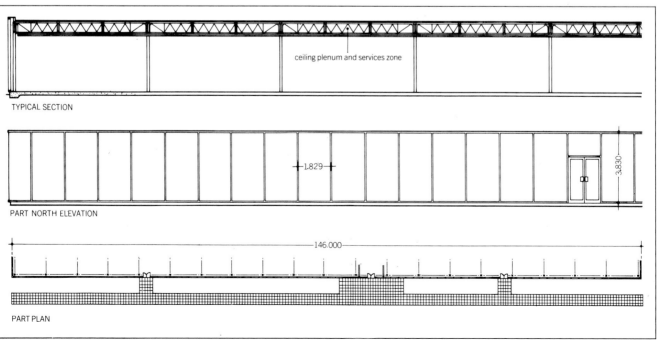

ceiling plenum and services zone

TYPICAL SECTION

1·829

3·830

PART NORTH ELEVATION

146·000

PART PLAN

3

2 Isometric detail showing the construction of the coping detail.
3 Typical section, part north elevation and part plan of the offices. The plan is the original one: the internal layout has since been changed, resulting in the main entrance now being in the east (short) elevation.
4 The relationship of the glazed curtain-wall to the structure is clearly and carefully articulated. The services are contained within the ceiling void.
5 Section through the external envelope of the building with, above, a plan detail of the mullion fixing cleat.

Credits
location Northern Road, Portsmouth, Hampshire
client IBM (United Kingdom)
architect Foster Associates
quantity surveyor GA Hanscomb Partnership
structural engineer Anthony Hunt Associates
services engineer RS Willcox Associates
acoustic consultant Engineering Design Consultants
main contractor Hawkins Construction (Southern) Ltd

Photo credit
Photographs by Richard Einzig.

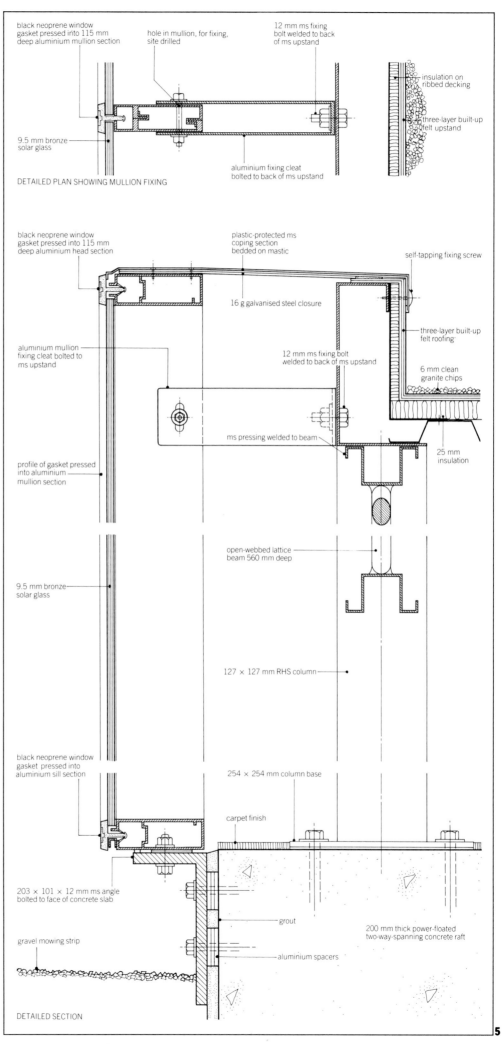

black neoprene window gasket pressed into 115 mm deep aluminium mullion section

hole in mullion, for fixing, site drilled

12 mm ms fixing bolt welded to back of ms upstand

insulation on ribbed decking

three-layer built-up felt upstand

9.5 mm bronze solar glass

aluminium fixing cleat bolted to back of ms upstand

DETAILED PLAN SHOWING MULLION FIXING

black neoprene window gasket pressed into 115 mm deep aluminium head section

plastic-protected ms coping section bedded on mastic

self-tapping fixing screw

16 g galvanised steel closure

three-layer built-up felt roofing

aluminium mullion fixing cleat bolted to ms upstand

12 mm ms fixing bolt welded to back of ms upstand

6 mm clean granite chips

ms pressing welded to beam

25 mm insulation

profile of gasket pressed into aluminium mullion section

open-webbed lattice beam 560 mm deep

9.5 mm bronze solar glass

127 × 127 mm RHS column

black neoprene window gasket pressed into aluminium sill section

254 × 254 mm column base

carpet finish

203 × 101 × 12 mm ms angle bolted to face of concrete slab

grout

gravel mowing strip

200 mm thick power-floated two-way-spanning concrete raft

aluminium spacers

DETAILED SECTION

EXTERNAL WALLS
WATERSPORTS CENTRE
Kit Allsopp Architects

Each type of external walling used in this building clearly reflects the function of the space behind it.

1 The building is designed to allow the best possible views out to the waterfront from this, the east elevation, and also out to the river in the opposite direction.

The external envelope to this building is formed from masonry walls on the ground floor, with appropriate windows marking particular spaces, and, to the upper floor mostly glazed walls allowing views to the waterfront and river.

At ground-floor level and part of the first-floor level the external walls are formed from London stock brick, an 80 mm cavity with 40 mm insulation, and an inner leaf of blockwork, either fairfaced or plastered.

There is a reference to the nautical theme in the use of a number of circular windows. These purpose-made aluminium windows are set in precast concrete surrounds cast in two halves (the central division is horizontal) and joined with two 12 × 150 mm ss dowels. The surrounds are smooth fairfaced concrete externally, but plain-finished internally to take a plaster finish. At the lowest point in the window surround a 20 mm wide × 10 mm deep sloping slot is cast in for drainage.

At ground-level there are also dpcs in each of the two leaves. The cavity is vented, filled up to ground level and sloped outwards, with weepholes provided to allow any water to escape. There could have been a problem here with cold bridging across the external wall through the floors which would have resulted in condensation internally. The use of foam-filled hollow precast planks should, however, reduce any cold bridge to a minimum.

The glazing to the upper floor is not high-tech glazing, but straightforward sheets of glass set in stained sw frames. Upper floor areas that are not glazed are clad with 7.5 mm thick waterproof-coated fibre cement panels fixed to 100 × 50 mm sw timber framing packed with insulation and clad internally with 12 mm thick building board.

The junction between the timber framing and the masonry below is formed with a hw sill fixed with gs fish-tail cramps. A dpc extends under the sill and 225 mm down into the face of the cavity. Water seepage under the sill is prevented by a continuous drip routed into the underside of the sill and a mastic joint at the junction of sill and brickwork. This detail is also protected by the extensive roof overhang and the balcony.

At first-floor level the projecting edge beams support the balcony which runs along the waterfront. 200 × 50 mm opepe planks are screw-fixed from below through pre-drilled holes to RSJs which sit on the concrete edge beams.

Where the steel beams project through the brickwork 10 mm thick ms plates are welded between the flanges to mask the joints. Heating pipes behind the ground-floor high-level concrete edge beam will help to counteract the cold bridging through the steel.

The opepe planks are laid with 5 mm gaps, and the joints in their lengths are staggered. The timber will gradually fade to a silvery colour. ■

Acknowledgment
The editors acknowledge the help of Lionel Friedland of Pentarch in the preparation of this article.

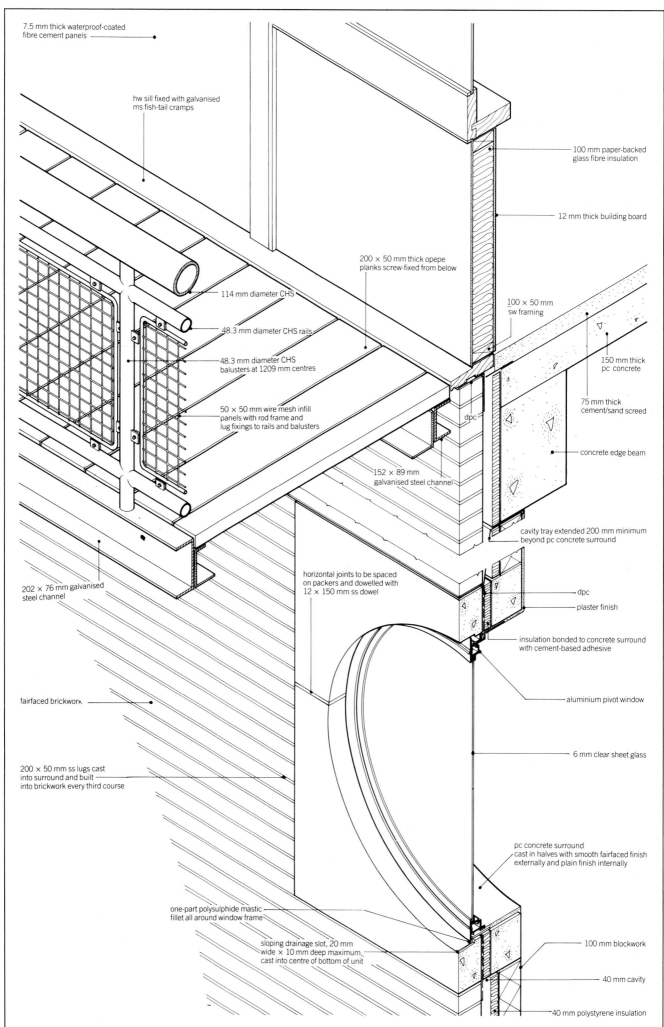

7.5 mm thick waterproof-coated
fibre cement panels

hw sill fixed with galvanised
ms fish-tail cramps

100 mm paper-backed
glass fibre insulation

12 mm thick building board

200 × 50 mm thick opepe
planks screw-fixed from below

100 × 50 mm
sw framing

150 mm thick
pc concrete

114 mm diameter CHS

48.3 mm diameter CHS rails

48.3 mm diameter CHS
balusters at 1209 mm centres

75 mm thick
cement/sand screed

dpc

50 × 50 mm wire mesh infill
panels with rod frame and
lug fixings to rails and balusters

concrete edge beam

152 × 89 mm
galvanised steel channel

cavity tray extended 200 mm minimum
beyond pc concrete surround

202 × 76 mm galvanised
steel channel

horizontal joints to be spaced
on packers and dowelled with
12 × 150 mm ss dowel

dpc

plaster finish

insulation bonded to concrete surround
with cement-based adhesive

aluminium pivot window

fairfaced brickwork

6 mm clear sheet glass

200 × 50 mm ss lugs cast
into surround and built
into brickwork every third course

pc concrete surround
cast in halves with smooth fairfaced finish
externally and plain finish internally

one-part polysulphide mastic
fillet all around window frame

sloping drainage slot, 20 mm
wide × 10 mm deep maximum,
cast into centre of bottom of unit

100 mm blockwork

40 mm cavity

40 mm polystyrene insulation

2

3

2 Cut-away isometric through the circular window and the balcony and glazed screen above.
3 Close-up of one bay on the east elevation showing the circular window to the manager's office, and the balcony in front of the lounge above.
4 Part-sections through the external wall on the waterfront elevation.

Credits
location West Ferry Road, London E14
client London Docklands Development Corporation
architect Kit Allsopp Architects: Kit Allsopp, Richard Russell, Peter Hughes, Brendan Phelan
quantity surveyor John Laing Construction, London Region
structural engineer Armand Safier and Partners: Derek Wood
services/mechanical and electrical services engineer Brian Sheed
main contractor John Laing Construction, London Region

Photo credit
Photographs by Charlotte Wood

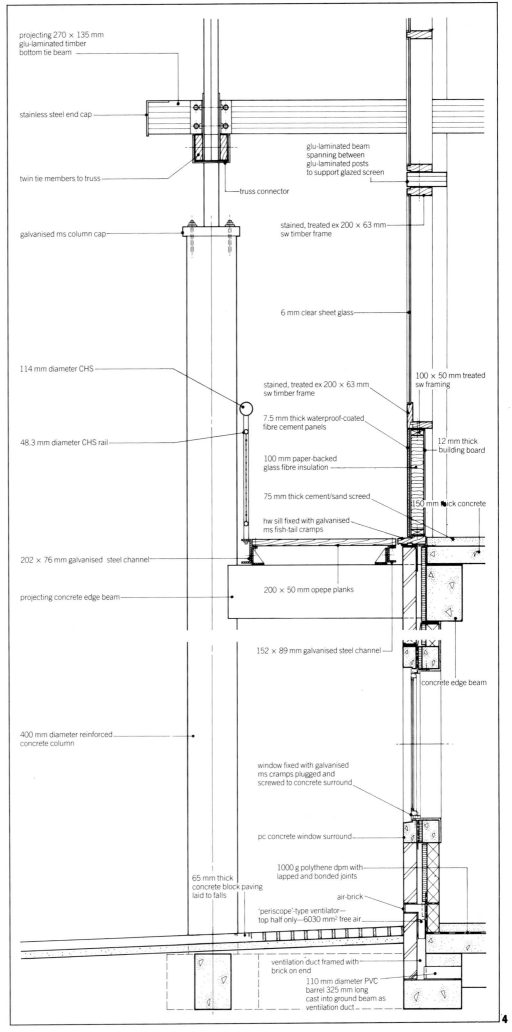

projecting 270 × 135 mm glu-laminated timber bottom tie beam

stainless steel end cap

twin tie members to truss

truss connector

glu-laminated beam spanning between glu-laminated posts to support glazed screen

galvanised ms column cap

stained, treated ex 200 × 63 mm sw timber frame

6 mm clear sheet glass

100 × 50 mm treated sw framing

114 mm diameter CHS

stained, treated ex 200 × 63 mm sw timber frame

7.5 mm thick waterproof-coated fibre cement panels

48.3 mm diameter CHS rail

100 mm paper-backed glass fibre insulation

12 mm thick building board

75 mm thick cement/sand screed

150 mm thick concrete

hw sill fixed with galvanised ms fish-tail cramps

202 × 76 mm galvanised steel channel

200 × 50 mm opepe planks

projecting concrete edge beam

152 × 89 mm galvanised steel channel

concrete edge beam

400 mm diameter reinforced concrete column

window fixed with galvanised ms cramps plugged and screwed to concrete surround

pc concrete window surround

1000 g polythene dpm with lapped and bonded joints

65 mm thick concrete block paving laid to falls

air-brick

'periscope'-type ventilator— top half only—6030 mm² free air

ventilation duct framed with brick on end

110 mm diameter PVC barrel 325 mm long cast into ground beam as ventilation duct

4

EXTERNAL WALLS
MEETING HALL
Edward Cullinan Architects

The external walls to this MacIntyre Foundation building are formed from purpose-designed, prefabricated timber cladding panels.

1 View of the hall from the south. The timber boarding is stained two shades of green, and the openable plywood panels are blue.

Acknowledgment
The editors acknowledge the help of John Campbell of Terry Farrell and Company and Lionel Friedland of Pentarch in the preparation of this article.

In designing the timber cladding panels for the MacIntyre Foundation buildings at Great Holm, an underlying principle for the architects was the manner in which the component trades were simply layered, using the nature of each material to achieve design objectives suitably while accommodating each material's tolerance demands.

Sitting on a brickwork semi-basement, the ground floor has a steel frame supporting the tiled roof, and, neatly fitting around the outside of the framing—so that there is no problem with cold bridges across the steelwork—are the prefabricated panel walls.

The basic stud-framed 4800 × 2360 mm panel includes six windows and a top-hung opening plywood panel to let in more light and fresh air if required. The 100 × 50 mm stud framework is clad internally with 12.5 mm plasterboard (with a vapour check behind) and externally with 12 mm thick sheathing ply. The cavities between the studs are packed with 100 mm installation.

The window joinery is fitted to the outside of this sandwich—allowing plenty of tolerance between the windows and the openings for them—and protected by a neat, unobtrusive, aluminium flashing at the window head. Simply profiled micropore painted sw frames are used for the windows, which accommodate a dry double-glazing system.

The external cladding to the panels, 20 mm thick lapped timber boarding stained inside and outside, is site-fixed across the joints in the panels. The horizontal boarding sits on 38 × 19 mm vertical sw battens on a breather membrane. The vertical boarding sits on 9 × 50 mm inert battens on top of the horizontal boarding and it is almost flush with the timber window sections.

The panels are anchored to the concrete floor with 200 × 150 mm angles. The vapour check membrane behind the plasterboard is dressed over the angle and under the insulation below the flooring. Panel-to-floor junctions are covered with conventional timber skirtings, and ply window lining junctions with plasterboard are covered with 25 mm half-round beads pinned to the ply, but no cover-piece is considered necessary at the window lining to window-case junctions.

The use of mastic is kept to a minimum: it is only used at the vertical junctions if the window, and the lead flashing on top of the panel, to ensure a watertight junction if there is movement in the timber window.

The simple, well-thought-through detailing ensured that the panels were straightforward to manufacture and install. The designer's aim, to produce an architecture that is constructionally elegant and that celebrates the joining and separation of materials in a considered and controlled way, has been met.

These panels are a welcome reminder that 'design for buildability' doesn't need to be an inferior or a less innovative design. ∎

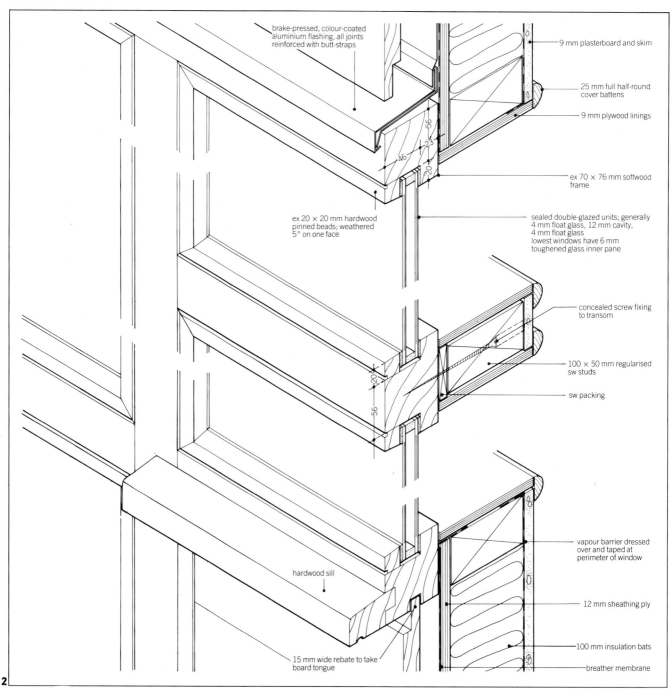

brake-pressed, colour-coated aluminium flashing, all joints reinforced with butt-straps

9 mm plasterboard and skim

25 mm full half-round cover battens

9 mm plywood linings

46 23 56

ex 70 × 76 mm softwood frame

ex 20 × 20 mm hardwood pinned beads; weathered 5° on one face

sealed double-glazed units; generally 4 mm float glass, 12 mm cavity, 4 mm float glass lowest windows have 6 mm toughened glass inner pane

concealed screw fixing to transom

200 56

100 × 50 mm regularised sw studs

sw packing

hardwood sill

vapour barrier dressed over and taped at perimeter of window

12 mm sheathing ply

100 mm insulation bats

breather membrane

15 mm wide rebate to take board tongue

2

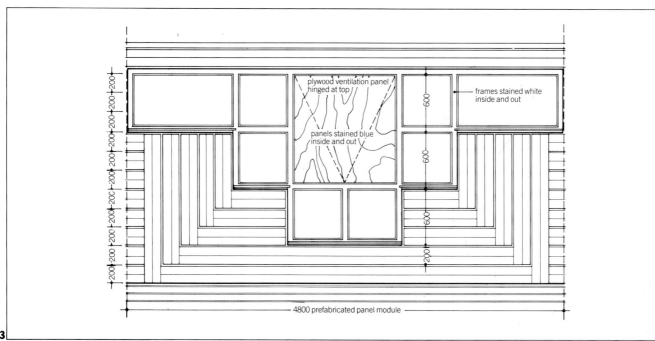

plywood ventilation panel hinged at top

frames stained white inside and out

panels stained blue inside and out

600

600

600

200

200 200 200 200 200 200 200 200 200 200 200 200

4800 prefabricated panel module

3

4

2 Isometric detail of part of a typical glazed timber panel.
3 Elevation of a typical panel. The glazing is fixed: it is the central plywood panel that opens for ventilation.
4 Close-up of an individual panel, showing the two thicknesses of lapped timber boarding and the glazed panels above.
5 Section through the external wall of the hall.

roofing felt

vapour barrier

concrete tile

12.5 mm plasterboard and skim

38 × 38 mm batten nailed to rafter

insulation

12 mm WBP ply; 4 No 50 mm dia holes with insect screen between rafters

100 × 63 mm double vacuum preservative-treated sw plate

150 × 150 mm UB drilled for fixing bolts

50 × 25 mm sw battens

9 mm WBP ply skirt, double vacuum preservative-treated and stained

sw filler batten treated as external boarding

225 × 50 mm double vacuum preservative-treated sw rafter

9 mm plasterboard and skim

brake-pressed, colour-coated aluminium flashing, all joints reinforced with butt-straps

9 mm plywood linings

ex 70 × 76 mm softwood frame

4 × 4 mm rebate

ex 20 × 20 mm hardwood pinned beads; weathered 5° on one face

PVC gutter and downpipe

steel column

sealed double-glazed units; generally 4 mm float glass, 12 mm cavity, 4 mm float glass lowest windows have 6 mm toughened glass inner pane

hardwood sill

25 mm full half-round cover battens

15 mm wide rebate to take board tongue

12 mm sheathing ply

sw skirting

hardwood flooring on 50 × 50 mm sw battens

38 × 19 mm vertical sw battens

100 mm breather membrane strip sandwiched between frames and plywood prior to fixing; edge left loose and dressed over site-fixed membrane

dpc

50 mm rigid insulation

200 × 150 mm restraining angle bolted to slab and sw framing

breather membrane

20 mm thick sw boarding on 38 × 19 mm sw battens, all double vacuum preservative treated

rc floor slab

5

Credits
location Haddon, Great Holm, Milton Keynes, Buckinghamshire
client MacIntyre Foundation
architects Edward Cullinan, Mark Beedle, Jeremy Stacey, Seán Harrington, Frances Holliss
quantity surveyor Ridge & Partners
structural engineer Jampel Davison and Bell
services engineers Max Fordham & Partners; James R. Briggs Associates
contractor Bushby construction

Photo credit
Photographs by Charlotte Wood

ROOFS AND PARAPETS
LAW COURTS
Evans and Shalev

The roofline of the Truro Courts of Justice building is dominated by two slate-covered rotundas with precast concrete parapet copings.

1 The large rotunda which sits above the waiting area for the Crown Courts. The clerestory glazing is of glass blocks. Small opening lights allow natural ventilation.

Acknowledgment
The editors acknowledge the help of John Campbell and Lionel Friedland of Terry Farrell Partnership and formerly of Bickerdike Allen Partners, in the preparation of this article.

The two conical rotundas, one large, one small, that top the major circulation spaces, form a landmark in the Truro skyline. The roofs are covered with local Delabole slates in diminishing courses and capped with anodised aluminium patent glazed lanterns.

Gutters are concealed behind low parapets that have projecting precast concrete raked copings, painted white. External faces of parapets are rough-cast rendered. The aggregate is crushed white marble. Between the wall plane and the copings a band of blue/black Staffordshire bricks pointed in white cement mortar forms a dentil course.

Slates are centre-fixed with copper nails on battens and counter battens above roofing felt on 12·5 mm Douglas Fir faced WBP ply screwed to 200 x 75 mm treated softwood rafters.

Rafters are set out radially and fixed by means of paired 10 mm thick steel plates welded to a continuous 229 x 76 mm RSC ring beam at the lantern and to 200 x 150 mm steel angles bolted to a reinforced concrete ring beam at the base. Rafters are braced by 50 x 50 mm herringbone struts at their mid point.

Above the RSC ring beam are two concentric continuous laminated timber rings 50 mm apart. The lantern glazing is fixed to the top of the larger, 250 x 50 mm section, ring which is coach bolted to 200 x 50 x 10 mm galvanised ms plates that are welded to the RSC ring beam at every third rafter. The smaller 100 x 40 mm section, outer ring forms an eaves upstand to which a lead-based flashing is fixed.

The roof space is vented between the two timber rings at the lantern and into the parapet wall cavity at the base through open perpends at 800 mm intervals in the lowest block course. The wall cavity is vented top and bottom through open perpends in the brick band courses.

Further detailed considerations include:
- flat roofed areas are built up above a reinforced concrete slab with: vapour barrier, lightweight concrete screed laid to falls, 13 mm sand and cement topping, hot bitumen bed on bitumen based primer, 35 mm Tekurat insulation board, 20 mm asphalt on isolating membrane, finished with rounded reflective chippings.
- rotunda gutters are lead-lined over building paper and sheathing felt on 25 mm WBP ply and are drained through concealed PVC downpipes.
- precast concrete copings are mastic pointed with a nominal 10 mm joint. Paint finish is a high build water-based microporous copolymer resin emulsion that contains fungicides to reduce algae growth.

External finishes are a response to the Cornish vernacular of blue/black slate and white painted rendered walls. Materials have been selected for their proven durability and low maintenance requirements. ■

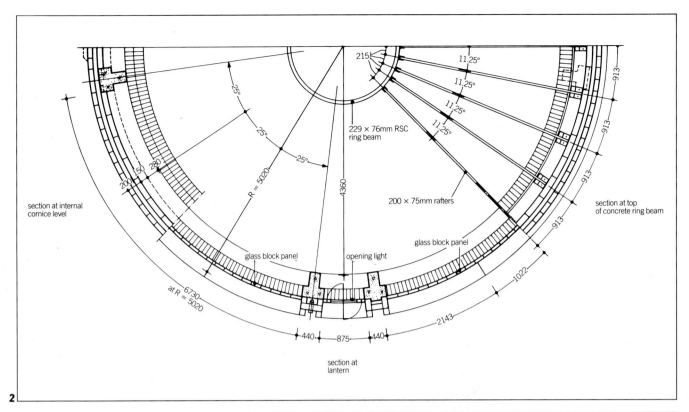

2

section at internal
cornice level

215

11.25°

11.25°

11.25°

11.25°

913

913

913

913

913

1022

229 × 76mm RSC
ring beam

25°

25°

25°

R = 5020

4360

200 × 75mm rafters

section at top
of concrete ring beam

200 150 280

glass block panel

opening light

glass block panel

at R = 6730
= 5020

440 875 440

2143

section at
lantern

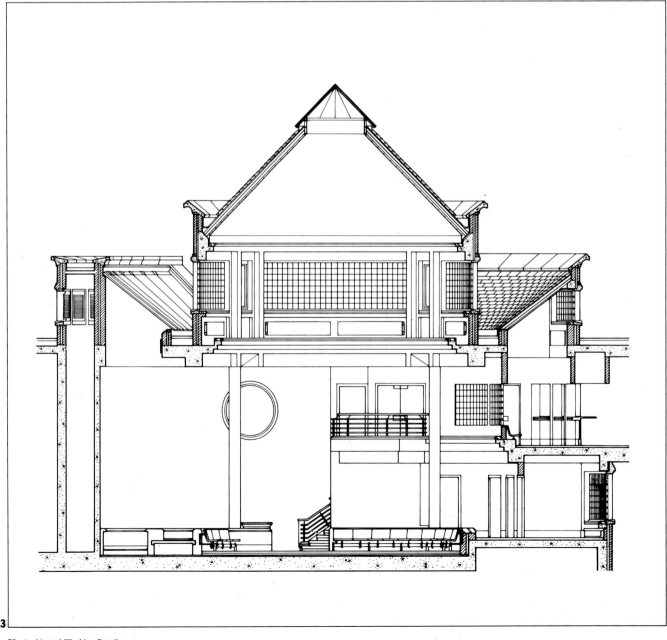

3

4

5

2 Plan of the large rotunda showing left, the section below the clerestory glazing; centre, through the glass block clerestory; right, through the parapet.
3 Section through large rotunda.
4 Slates are laid in diminishing courses. Lanterns are of anodised aluminium patent glazing.
5 View of the rotunda ceiling showing clerestory and lantern.
6 Roof section at lantern and parapet. Precast concrete lintels above clerestory glazing are bolted to continuous stainless steel angles. Constant warm air flow from radiators below the clerestory glazing prevents condensation at the glass blocks and lintels which are potential cold bridges.

Credits
location Edward Street, Truro
architects Evans and Shalev; Eldred Evans, David Shalev, Charles Mador
quantity surveyor MDA; Richard Pope, Kevin Heaton
structural engineer Anthony Hunt Associates; Stephen Morley, Alan Smith
services engineer Max Fordham and Partners, Max Fordham, David Lindsay
contractor Dudley Coles
contract manager Bryan Hammond
site agent Tony Luke
clerk of works Wilf Ballm
project managers, Property Services Agency, Martin Brooks, John Whiting, Jim Dunaway, Len Froom-Lewis
lightning protection WM & RW Bacon
Glassblock windows Luxcrete London
rooflights TMV Group, Beckenham.
slate roofing Forrester roofing
asphalt Clegg and Shortman
laminated timber beams Cowley Structural Timberwork, Lincoln
Precast concrete products W J Ladd, Redruth

Photo credit
Photography Martin Charles

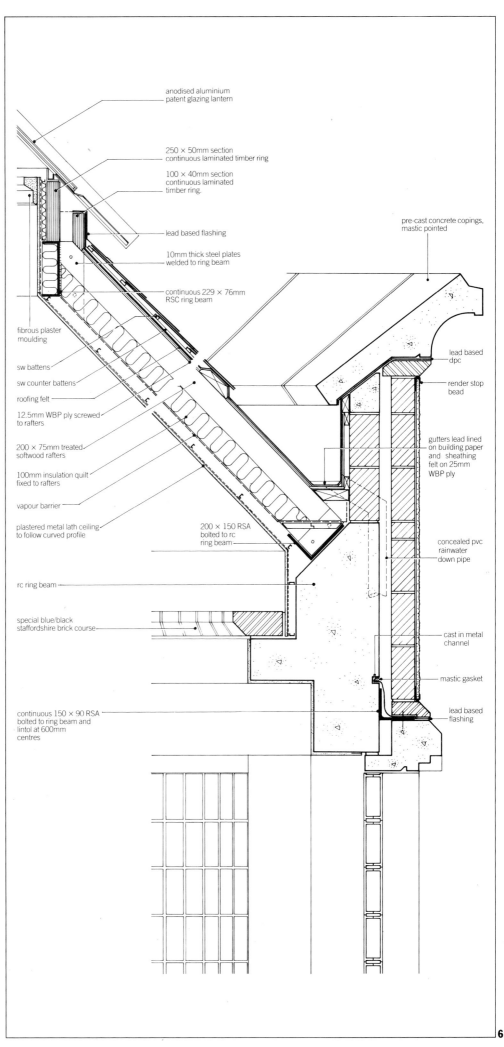

anodised aluminium patent glazing lantern

250 × 50mm section continuous laminated timber ring

100 × 40mm section continuous laminated timber ring.

lead based flashing

10mm thick steel plates welded to ring beam

continuous 229 × 76mm RSC ring beam

pre-cast concrete copings, mastic pointed

fibrous plaster moulding

sw battens

sw counter battens

roofing felt

12.5mm WBP ply screwed to rafters

200 × 75mm treated softwood rafters

100mm insulation quilt fixed to rafters

vapour barrier

plastered metal lath ceiling to follow curved profile

200 × 150 RSA bolted to rc ring beam

rc ring beam

special blue/black staffordshire brick course

continuous 150 × 90 RSA bolted to ring beam and lintol at 600mm centres

lead based dpc

render stop bead

gutters lead lined on building paper and sheathing felt on 25mm WBP ply

concealed pvc rainwater down pipe

cast in metal channel

mastic gasket

lead based flashing

6

ROOF AND EAVES
WAREHOUSE AND OFFICES
Denton Scott Associates

A metal deck pitched roof, with deep overhanging eaves, on the warehouse and office building for Schwarzkopf is supported on a tubular steel structure.

1

1 Warehouses and office areas are distinguished by different treatment of the external walls; solid blockwork for the warehouse, and full glazing for the offices. A single roof with propped oversailing eaves unites the two elements.

The building is a shed structure that combines 1880 m² of double-height warehouse space at the rear with two floors of offices linked to an existing building at the front.

The primary structure is a tubular steel frame. A triangulated spine truss runs the length of the plan supported on CHS aisle columns at 10.8 m centres. Lateral trusses span 14.4 m at 5.4 m centres between the spine truss and internally placed perimeter columns.

The blockwork external walls stop short of the roof and are braced by external piers on the 5.4 m longitudinal column grid. A continuous 203 × 203 mm UC ring beam on top of the walls has tubular steel connections to the perimeter columns, tying the steel and masonry structures together.

An 1100 mm deep band of frameless eaves glazing provides an important visual separation—the roof appears to float free of the walls—and together with the central rooflight, lets daylight into the warehouse.

Deep overhanging eaves shelter the blockwork walls. The long edge of the roof deck is supported by a 600 mm wide folded-steel gutter, propped from below by triangulated eaves canopy steelwork that connects to the ends of the trusses and is raked at an angle of 49° from shoe-plates bolted to padstones on top of the piers.

The roof and structural components are articulated by colour coding. Primary elements—columns and tubular steelwork—are bright green. Secondary elements—gutters, ring beam and purlins—are dark blue. Tertiary elements—roof deck sheets, downpipes and patent glazing bars—are grey.

Further detailed considerations include:
● mild steel components, including gutters, are not galvanised. Paintwork specification is intended to give maximum protection in exposed conditions. Steelwork was blast-cleaned followed by one coat two-pack phosphate epoxy primer, one coat high-build epoxy micaceous iron oxide, finished with two-coat luxol silicone alkyd enamel according to colour coding
● the roof pitch at 6.366° is very shallow and is roofed in single-sheet lengths to avoid horizontal lapped joints which could be vulnerable to wind-blown rain-water. Vertical sheet joints, cloaks and flashings are all silicone-sealed
● the inner profiled metal roofing sheet acts as a vapour barrier. All joints and fixing holes are silicone-sealed.

Services and fabric are well co-ordinated. Smoke vents and exhaust air extract for high-level gas heaters suspended from the lateral trusses in warehouse areas are located in the patent glazed ridge rooflight. Rain-water pipes occur on the 5.4 m grid, housed within the external blockwork piers where they both mask the expansion joint and reinforce the structural rhythm of the facades. ■

Acknowledgment
The editors acknowledge the help of John Campbell of Terry Farrell and Company and Lionel Friedland of Pentarch in the preparation of this article.

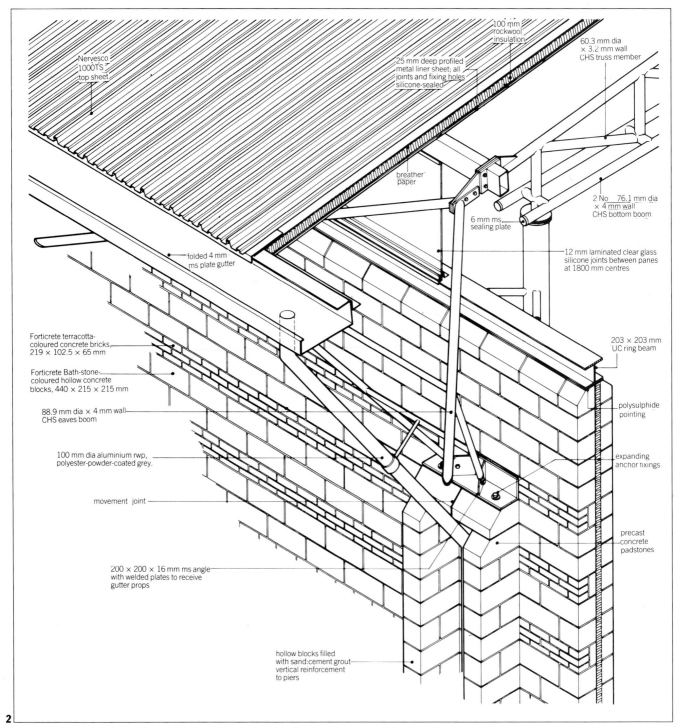

2

Nervesco 1000TS top sheet

100 mm rockwool insulation

25 mm deep profiled metal liner sheet; all joints and fixing holes silicone-sealed

60.3 mm dia × 3.2 mm wall CHS truss member

breather paper

6 mm ms sealing plate

2 No 76.1 mm dia × 4 mm wall CHS bottom boom

folded 4 mm ms plate gutter

12 mm laminated clear glass silicone joints between panes at 1800 mm centres

Forticrete terracotta-coloured concrete bricks, 219 × 102.5 × 65 mm

Forticrete Bath-stone-coloured hollow concrete blocks, 440 × 215 × 215 mm

88.9 mm dia × 4 mm wall CHS eaves boom

100 mm dia aluminium rwp, polyester-powder-coated grey.

movement joint

200 × 200 × 16 mm ms angle with welded plates to receive gutter props

hollow blocks filled with sand:cement grout-vertical reinforcement to piers

203 × 203 mm UC ring beam

polysulphide pointing

expanding anchor fixings

precast concrete padstones

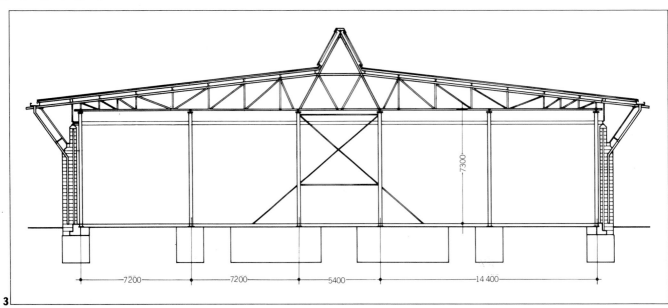

3

7200 — 7200 — 5400 — 14 400

7300

2 Cut-away isometric of the structural eaves steelwork and gutter assembly. Rain-water pipes are housed between blockwork pier projections which brace the external walls.
3 Cross-section through the double-height warehouse.
4, 5 Detail of blockwork pier and triangulated eaves steelwork. Piers occur on the structural steelwork grid at 5.4 m intervals along each elevation. Rain-water pipes mask the expansion joint in the centre of each pier and reinforce the structural rhythm of the facades.
6 Detailed section at eaves.
7 Detailed section at ridge.

Credits
location Penn Road, Aylesbury, Bucks
client Schwarzkopf
architects Denton Scott Associates
design director Andrew Scott
project architect Robert de Grey
assistant architects Adrian Morrow, Chris Bannister
quantity surveyors Davis Langdon and Everest
structure and services Buro Happold
main contractors Western Counties Construction
subcontractors, steel frame Sheetfabs, Nottingham
window walls Dean & Amos Aluminium Systems
patent glazing Lyngrid Contracts
roof cladding Nervesco

Photo credit
Photographs by Peter Cook.

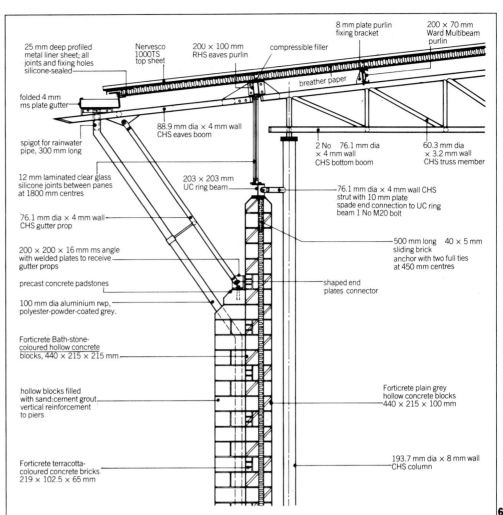

- 25 mm deep profiled metal liner sheet; all joints and fixing holes silicone-sealed
- Nervesco 1000TS top sheet
- 200 × 100 mm RHS eaves purlin
- compressible filler
- 8 mm plate purlin fixing bracket
- 200 × 70 mm Ward Multibeam purlin
- breather paper
- folded 4 mm ms plate gutter
- 88.9 mm dia × 4 mm wall CHS eaves boom
- 2 No 76.1 mm dia × 4 mm wall CHS bottom boom
- 60.3 mm dia × 3.2 mm wall CHS truss member
- spigot for rainwater pipe, 300 mm long
- 203 × 203 mm UC ring beam
- 76.1 mm dia × 4 mm wall CHS strut with 10 mm plate spade end connection to UC ring beam 1 No M20 bolt
- 12 mm laminated clear glass silicone joints between panes at 1800 mm centres
- 76.1 mm dia × 4 mm wall CHS gutter prop
- 200 × 200 × 16 mm ms angle with welded plates to receive gutter props
- precast concrete padstones
- shaped end plates connector
- 500 mm long 40 × 5 mm sliding brick anchor with two full ties at 450 mm centres
- 100 mm dia aluminium rwp, polyester-powder-coated grey.
- Forticrete Bath-stone-coloured hollow concrete blocks, 440 × 215 × 215 mm
- hollow blocks filled with sand:cement grout vertical reinforcement to piers
- Forticrete plain grey hollow concrete blocks 440 × 215 × 100 mm
- Forticrete terracotta-coloured concrete bricks 219 × 102.5 × 65 mm
- 193.7 mm dia × 8 mm wall CHS column

6

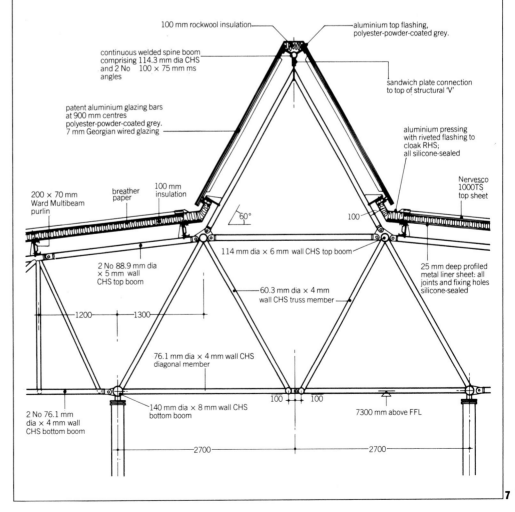

- 100 mm rockwool insulation
- aluminium top flashing, polyester-powder-coated grey.
- continuous welded spine boom comprising 114.3 mm dia CHS and 2 No 100 × 75 mm ms angles
- sandwich plate connection to top of structural 'V'
- patent aluminium glazing bars at 900 mm centres polyester-powder-coated grey. 7 mm Georgian wired glazing
- aluminium pressing with riveted flashing to cloak RHS; all silicone-sealed
- Nervesco 1000TS top sheet
- 200 × 70 mm Ward Multibeam purlin
- breather paper
- 100 mm insulation
- 60°
- 100
- 114 mm dia × 6 mm wall CHS top boom
- 2 No 88.9 mm dia × 5 mm wall CHS top boom
- 60.3 mm dia × 4 mm wall CHS truss member
- 25 mm deep profiled metal liner sheet: all joints and fixing holes silicone-sealed
- 1200
- 1300
- 76.1 mm dia × 4 mm wall CHS diagonal member
- 2 No 76.1 mm dia × 4 mm wall CHS bottom boom
- 140 mm dia × 8 mm wall CHS bottom boom
- 100
- 100
- 7300 mm above FFL
- 2700
- 2700

7

TIMBER STRUCTURE
LEISURE POOL
Alsop & Lyall

The structural use of glu-laminated timber at Alsop and Lyall's Sheringham Leisure Pool is both elegant and inventive.

1

1 View down the pool hall. The trellis-like glu-laminated columns are conceived as landscape elements and will eventually be overgrown by climbing plants. The columns support bow-string trusses.

The building is a single storey aisled structure, with a symmetrical, classical plan, emphasised by the line of timber lattice columns running along each side of the pool. Columns are at 4·8 m centres and sit on 1·6 m high, tiled concrete plinths. The columns support bow string trusses that span 18·6 m. Truss and column members are of glu-laminated European whitewood with the exception of the outer truss struts, packers and chocks which are of hardwood.

The lattice columns are conceived as elements in the overall architectural 'landscape' and will eventually be overgrown with foliage from vines planted in boxes let into the top of the concrete plinths. The key consideration was to keep member sizes to a minimum to achieve a trellis-like effect.

As a single storey building there was no requirement for structural fire resistance or for oversizing of members to allow for sacrificial charring. Joints are either lapped or butted and secured by galvanised mild steel bolts and plates.

The most complex junction is at the column head where the aisle beam, tie beam and associated diagonal strut and knee brace converge. Structurally, the braces need maximum strength in the middle, which allowed them to be tapered in a 'cricket bat' profile. The slender ends are more easily accommodated at the column junction.

Placing the lattice columns on concrete plinths reduced the length of timber members and allowed cross-bracing and section sizes to be minimalised. The plinths are high enough to prevent children climbing up the ladder-like columns, and protect the timber from contact with pool water.

Further detailed considerations include:
- all structural timber was double vacuum preservative treated to achieve a 60-year design life and coated internally with two coats of microporous exterior grade wood stain. Finish colours are white to softwood and clear to hardwood elements. Externally exposed bow-rafter ends are stained 'light oak' with an extra coating to the end grain
- glu-laminated timber is an excellent material for chemically hostile swimming pool environments
- connecting bolts, plates and straps are of galvanised mild steel. Stainless steel is more resistant to chemical attack but was too expensive
- all galvanised metalwork is protected with two coats of chlorinated rubber paint
- the structure is cross-braced by mild steel tubes fixed between truss tie-beams.

Using glu-laminated timber, any size of cross-section, profile or length of member can be produced. The only limiting factors are manufacturing space and transportation. As members are factory-produced, high standards of quality, accuracy and finish can be achieved. ■

Acknowledgment
The editors acknowledge the help of John Campbell and Lionel Friedland of Terry Farrell Partnership and formerly of Bickerdike Allen Partners, in the preparation of this article.

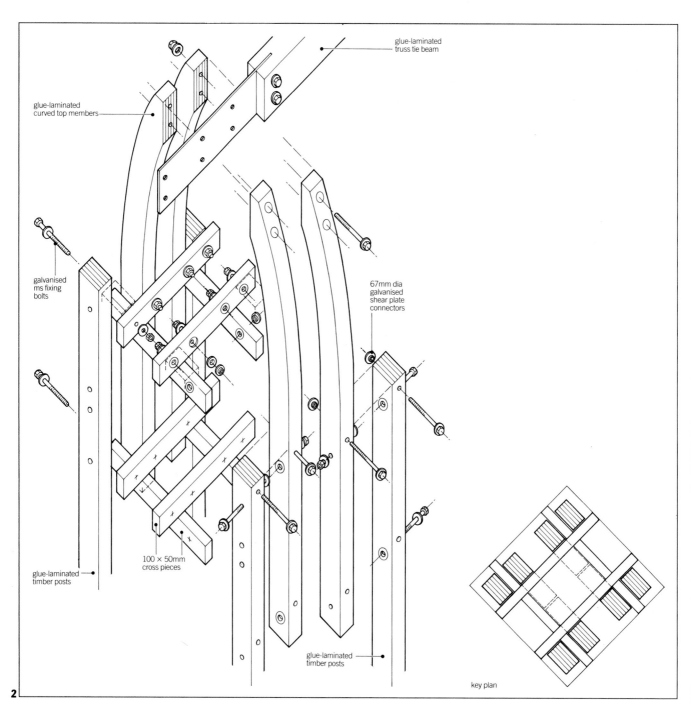

glue-laminated
truss tie beam

glue-laminated
curved top members

galvanised
ms fixing
bolts

67mm dia
galvanised
shear plate
connectors

100 × 50mm
cross pieces

glue-laminated
timber posts

glue-laminated
timber posts

key plan

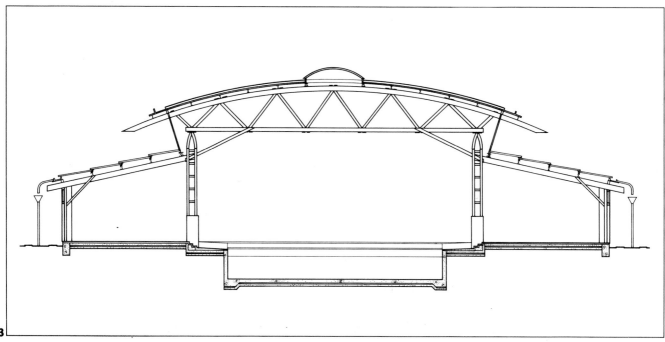

2

3

4

5

6

2 Exploded axonometric of column head assembly, where the aisle beam, tie beam and associated diagonal strut and kneebrace converge.

3 Cross-section through the building showing position of columns and bow-string trusses. Above the lower side aisles the roof is supported by glu-laminated rafters which sit on glu-laminated timber posts at the external walls. Posts are held clear of the floor on galvanised steel shoes.

4, 5 Photographs taken during construction, before the timber walling was erected.

6 Knee braces have a 'cricket bat' profile: the ends are tapered so that they can be more easily accommodated at the column head junction.

7 Elevations of column head and base.

Credits
location Sheringham, Norfolk
client Clifford Barnett Group for Norfolk District Council
architects William Alsop and John Lyall
project architect Peter Clash
assistant architects Mike Waddington, Simon North, Jonathan Adams, Isabelle Lousada
quantity surveyor Drysdale de Leeuw and Partners
structural engineer Anthony Hunt Associates
management contractor Clugston Construction
frame Kingston Craftsmen (1981)

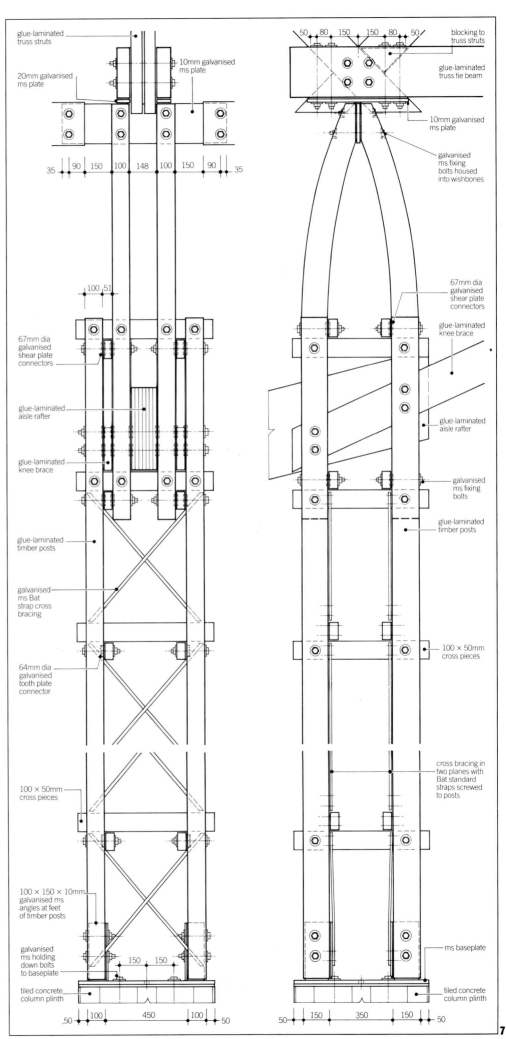

glue-laminated truss struts
10mm galvanised ms plate
20mm galvanised ms plate
blocking to truss struts
glue-laminated truss tie beam
10mm galvanised ms plate
galvanised ms fixing bolts housed into wishbones
67mm dia galvanised shear plate connectors
glue-laminated knee brace
67mm dia galvanised shear plate connectors
glue-laminated aisle rafter
glue-laminated aisle rafter
glue-laminated knee brace
galvanised ms fixing bolts
glue-laminated timber posts
glue-laminated timber posts
galvanised ms Bat strap cross bracing
100 × 50mm cross pieces
64mm dia galvanised tooth plate connector
100 × 50mm cross pieces
cross bracing in two planes with Bat standard straps screwed to posts
100 × 150 × 10mm galvanised ms angles at feet of timber posts
galvanised ms holding down bolts to baseplate
ms baseplate
tiled concrete column plinth
tiled concrete column plinth

SERVICED FLOOR
RECORDING EQUIPMENT FACTORY
Michael Hopkins and Partners

The Solid State Logic factory has services ducted through the raised floor void above a coffered concrete slab with an exposed soffit to which combined ventilation and lighting fittings are mounted.

1

1 The building is naturally ventilated through opening sliding panels in the full-height perimeter glazing. Additional air movement in the deep plan and fresh air in the winter months is supplied through air diffusers incorporated in the light fittings.

Acknowledgement
The editors acknowledge the help of Roland Gibbard of YRM Interiors in the preparation of this article.

The building has two storeys and a square plan with a central top-lit atrium. It can be naturally ventilated through sliding units in the full-height perimeter glazing and electrically operated, thermostatically controlled opening rooflights. Permanent mechanical ventilation—not air-conditioning—is provided to maintain air movement in the deep plan and supply fresh air to the occupants. Heating is by means of low-temperature hot water natural convectors in trenches around the perimeter of each floor. Plant rooms are on the ground floor.

Services distribution is via a 400 mm void below a standard 600 mm modular raised deck at first floor level. Supply and return air to and from the ground floor is ducted to supply diffusers incorporated in the light fittings and from return air bellmouths above the light fittings.

Fresh air to the first floor is fed via the floor void, which acts as a plenum, to circular grilles in the floor panels. Grilles and panels can be easily relocated to suit furniture and compartment layouts. First floor return air is ducted from extract points above the perforated suspended metal ceiling.

Lighting cables are loose-laid in the floor void. Power, data and telecom distribution to the ground and first floors is via a three-compartment floor trunking system.

The floor slab is of white in-situ concrete. Shallow domed coffers are set out on a 1·8 m grid. The soffit was lightly grit-blasted to remove a patchy gloss finish left by the surface of the grp formwork and to expose the Portland stone aggregate.

Lighting on the ground floor is by purpose-designed luminaires with low-energy compact fluorescent tubes and control gear adapted from standard fittings, above a 1 m diameter etched glass disc mounted in the floor slab coffers. An overall surface illuminance of 400 lux on the working plane is achieved. Local task lighting was supplied by the client.

Further detailed considerations include:
● glass discs and fluorescent fittings are suspended on four stainless steel wires with adjustable terminals, anchored to the slab soffit by expanding threaded fixings
● two release terminals on each disc allow the glass to be dropped for change of lamps
● the outline of the fluorescent tubes is clearly visible through the glass, which detracts from the overall appearance
● insects and dust will build up on the upper surface of the glass without regular cleaning.

Generally the building relies on standard components, the ground floor light fittings being the only significant one-off. Special fittings require much testing and thought in order to improve on the quality of well proven standard products. In this case an ingenious solution to lighting and ventilation distribution has been achieved, but will require a high standard of maintenance. ■

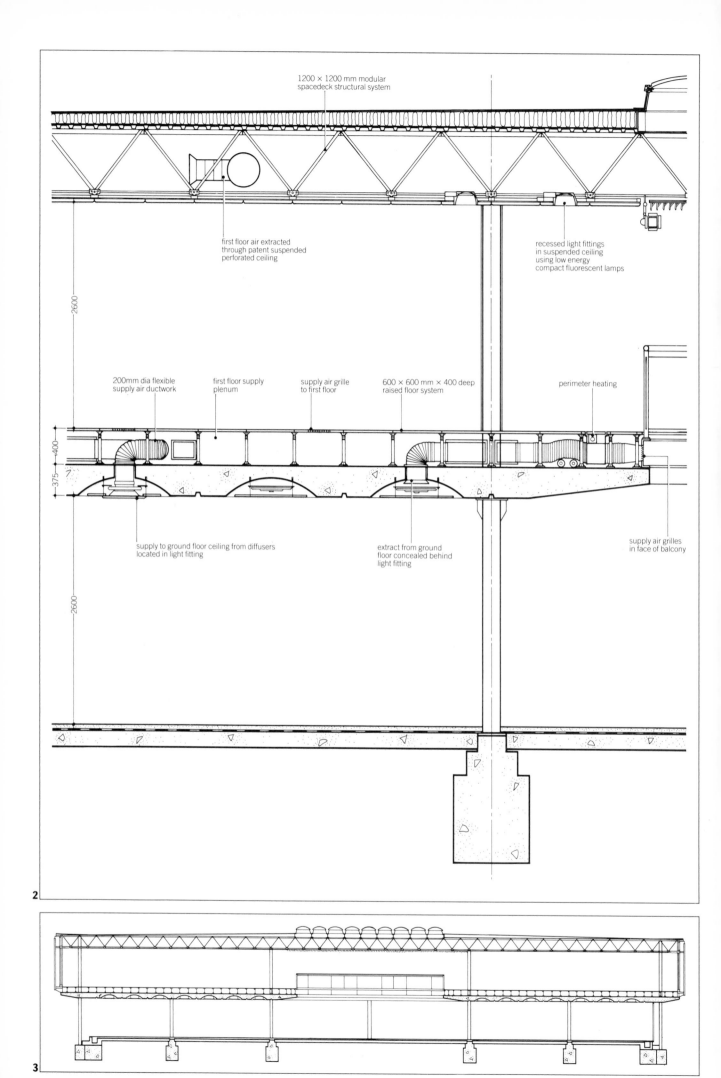

1200 × 1200 mm modular
spacedeck structural system

first floor air extracted
through patent suspended
perforated ceiling

recessed light fittings
in suspended ceiling
using low energy
compact fluorescent lamps

2600

200mm dia flexible
supply air ductwork

first floor supply
plenum

supply air grille
to first floor

600 × 600 mm × 400 deep
raised floor system

perimeter heating

400

375

supply to ground floor ceiling from diffusers
located in light fitting

extract from ground
floor concealed behind
light fitting

supply air grilles
in face of balcony

2600

2

3

4

5

2 Section showing the relationship between supply and extract air equipment and light fittings in the first floor slab soffit and location of floor supply grilles and high-level extract equipment on the first floor.
3 Cross-section through the deep plan building which has a central top-lit atrium.
4, 5 The typical light fitting is an etched glass disc suspended in the domed coffers of the concrete slab. Supply air diffusers are incorporated in some fittings, 5.
6 Section through a typical fitting with an extract air bellmouth above.
7 Section through a combined supply air diffuser and light fitting.

Credits
location Springhill Road, Begbroke, Oxon
client Solid State Logic
architect Michael Hopkins and Partners
partners in charge Michael Hopkins, Ian Sharratt
project architect Peter Romaniuk
assistant architects Peter Cartwright, Bill Dunster, Graham Saunders
quantity surveyor Davis Langdon and Everest, Alec Waller, Clive Lewis
structural and services engineer Buro Happold, M Dickson, Michael Green, Peter Moseley
main contractor Walter Lawrence Project Management
project manager Peter Richardson
mechanical/plumbing Alden Heating
electrical services Drake and Skull Engineering
in-situ concrete Whelan and Grant
in-situ concrete formwork Barnes Plastics
raised floors Floorplan Electrical

Photo credit
Photographs by Martin Charles

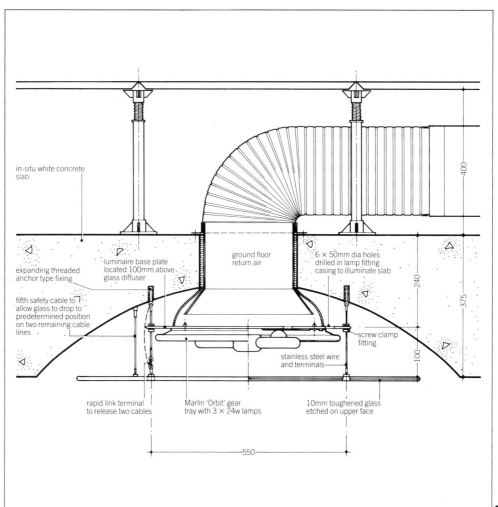

in-situ white concrete slab

luminaire base plate located 100mm above glass diffuser

expanding threaded anchor type fixing

fifth safety cable to allow glass to drop to predetermined position on two remaining cable lines

ground floor return air

6 × 50mm dia holes drilled in lamp fitting casing to illuminate slab

screw clamp fitting

stainless steel wire and terminals

rapid link terminal to release two cables

Marlin 'Orbit' gear tray with 3 × 24w lamps

10mm toughened glass etched on upper face

400

240

375

100

550

6

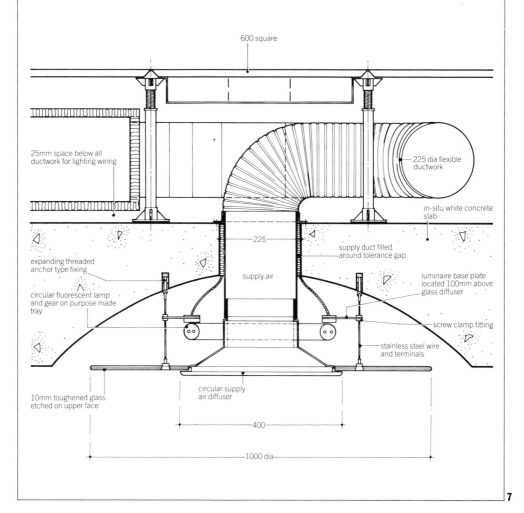

600 square

25mm space below all ductwork for lighting wiring

225 dia flexible ductwork

in-situ white concrete slab

expanding threaded anchor type fixing

225

supply duct filled around tolerance gap

supply air

luminaire base plate located 100mm above glass diffuser

circular fluorescent lamp and gear on purpose made tray

screw clamp fitting

stainless steel wire and terminals

10mm toughened glass etched on upper face

circular supply air diffuser

400

1000 dia

7

STEEL STRUCTURE
SCHOOL OF ARCHITECTURE
Dave King and Rod McAllister

The Liverpool School of Architecture's steel superstructure demonstrates a variety of joints and structural principles, yet maintains a visual elegance.

1

1 The metal deck roof is supported on tapered steel beams with holes cut in the web. The frame is stiffened by welded RHS cross-bracing in one bay.

The new school fills the courtyard of an existing building on two levels and roofs over the entire plan area with a steel frame structure. The floors and columns of the lower two levels are in reinforced concrete with piled foundations.

The steel structure is designed as a system of columns and beams arranged on the half-grid of the concrete frame below. The beams are pin-jointed to the CHS columns laterally and the columns joined longitudinally by site-welded RHS struts to form a continuous portal. The portal tends to be stiffer where shorter columns are placed over the existing structure; therefore, to transfer wind loading back to the concrete core, a braced bay is introduced which shifts the portal's point of maximum stiffness away from the existing brickwork and foundations.

The braced bay also accommodates horizontal roof bracing and wind bracing to the triangular rooflight above. Further bracing is provided by raking struts at the perimeter and paired A-frames with a horizontal K-brace at terrace level.

The I-section roof beams are set out on the existing building grid at 3·15 m centres. They are tapered at the ends and raked on the top flange to give a roof fall of 1:40.

Beams are constructed from 12 mm and 8 mm ms plate guillotined to profile and continuously shop-welded. Holes in the webs were cut by hand and all welds ground flush before priming. The bottom flange stabilising struts are made from CHSs with ends press-brake flattened prior to profiling and drilling.

Further detailed considerations include:
● pinned beams to column joints express the hinged frame but lose the advantages of structural continuity by articulating the beams
● fabrication methods used by a small local firm were labour-intensive but proved fast and economical (40 per cent of tender price submitted by major firms) due to their experience, and achieved a high standard of craftsmanship
● all metalwork was primed with micaceous iron oxide and finished with silicon alkyd aluminium paint, which is more chalk-resistant than conventional silver paints
● the structure employs a variety of steel sections, used for maximum performance and cheapness and also to clearly articulate structural elements for teaching purposes.

The structure achieves a clear build-up of elements within an almost Classical order. Columns have expressed bases and capitals, beams span between columns, purlins follow visual as well as structural lines and the roof decking span is clearly defined. The valley gutters are centralised above the columns, and end with a hopper head and downpipe 'column' visible through slot windows on the column grid line. ■

Acknowledgment
The editors acknowledge the help of John Winter of John Winter and Associates in the preparation of this article.

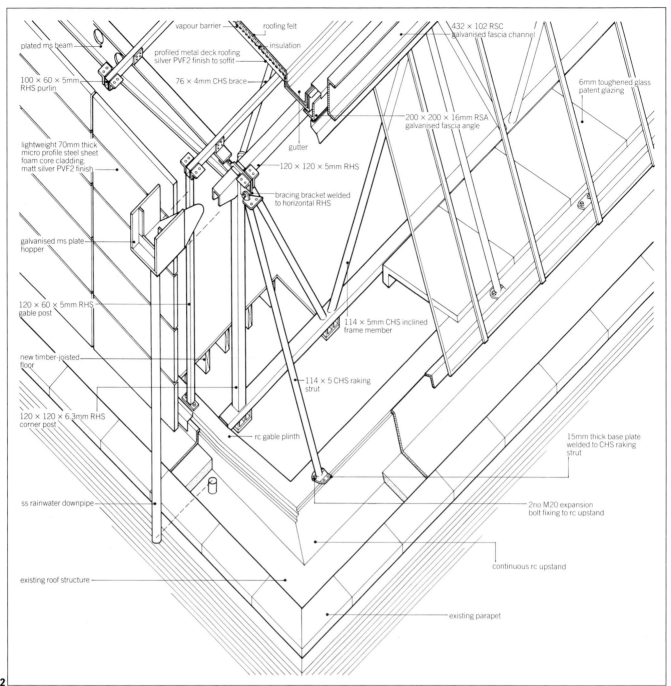

2

plated ms beam

100 × 60 × 5mm RHS purlin

vapour barrier

roofing felt

insulation

profiled metal deck roofing silver PVF2 finish to soffit

76 × 4mm CHS brace

432 × 102 RSC galvanised fascia channel

6mm toughened glass patent glazing

200 × 200 × 16mm RSA galvanised fascia angle

gutter

120 × 120 × 5mm RHS

bracing bracket welded to horizontal RHS

lightweight 70mm thick micro profile steel sheet foam core cladding. matt silver PVF2 finish

galvanised ms plate hopper

120 × 60 × 5mm RHS gable post

114 × 5mm CHS inclined frame member

114 × 5 CHS raking strut

new timber-joisted floor

120 × 120 × 6.3mm RHS corner post

rc gable plinth

15mm thick base plate welded to CHS raking strut

ss rainwater downpipe

2no M20 expansion bolt fixing to rc upstand

continuous rc upstand

existing roof structure

existing parapet

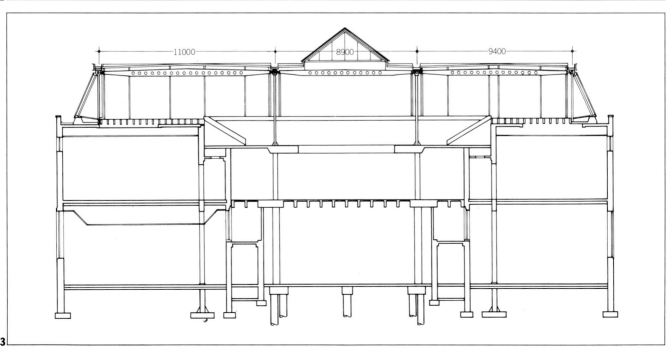

3

11000   8900   9400

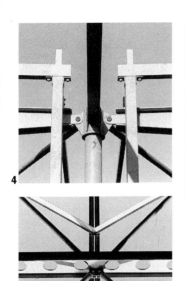

4

5

2 Axonometric of steelwork and cladding assembly at the gable end.
3 Cross-section through the new studio showing inclined perimeter glazing and triangular central rooflight.
4, 5 Construction photographs of beam and cross-bracing junctions at the gable end, 4, and rooflight, 5.
6 Isometric column and beam assembly with plans inset. Columns have clearly described capitals and bases. The plated beams are pin-jointed at the column heads to express the laterally hinged frame. RHS ties were site-welded to form a continuous longitudinal portal.

Credits
location Abercromby Square, Liverpool
client University of Liverpool
architects Dave King and Rod McAllister in association with the Gerald Beech Partnership
quantity surveyors John Dansken & Purdie, Gordon Lees, Alan Kennaugh
M & E services University of Liverpool, Building Services Department, Dave Dutton, Henry Gun-why
structural engineers Roy Billington Associates, John Dale, Dave Harding
main contractor A. Monk Building and Civil Engineering
site agent Tim Langley
resident quantity surveyor Ian Pickering
steelwork Royden Engineering
MIO paint Leighs paints
silicon alkyd aluminium Croda Paints

Photo credit
1, Julie Phipps; 4,5, courtesy of the architects.

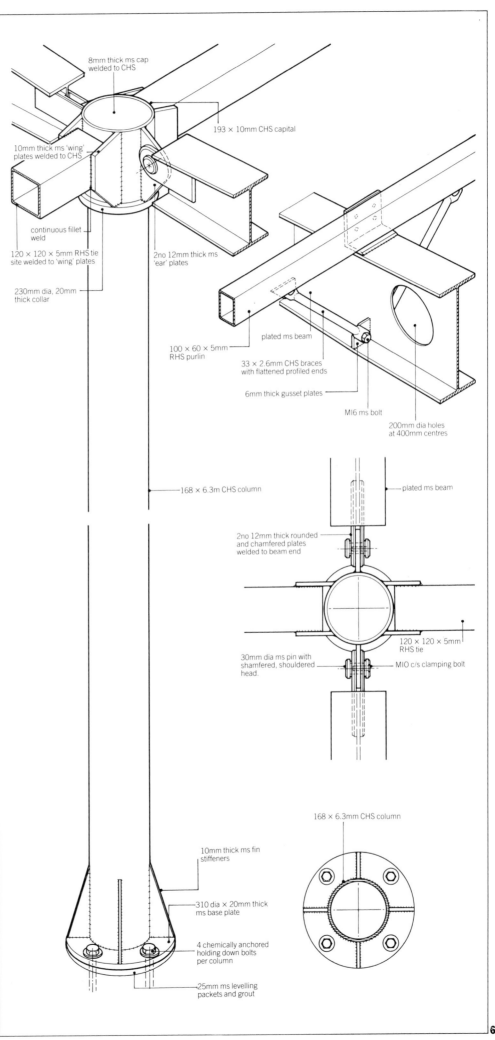

8mm thick ms cap welded to CHS

193 × 10mm CHS capital

10mm thick ms 'wing' plates welded to CHS

continuous fillet weld

120 × 120 × 5mm RHS tie site welded to 'wing' plates

230mm dia, 20mm thick collar

2no 12mm thick ms 'ear' plates

plated ms beam

100 × 60 × 5mm RHS purlin

33 × 2.6mm CHS braces with flattened profiled ends

6mm thick gusset plates

MI6 ms bolt

200mm dia holes at 400mm centres

168 × 6.3m CHS column

plated ms beam

2no 12mm thick rounded and chamfered plates welded to beam end

120 × 120 × 5mm RHS tie

30mm dia ms pin with shamfered, shouldered head.

MIO c/s clamping bolt

10mm thick ms fin stiffeners

310 dia × 20mm thick ms base plate

4 chemically anchored holding down bolts per column

25mm ms levelling packets and grout

168 × 6.3mm CHS column

TEMPORARY STRUCTURE
RETAIL OUTLET
Terry Farrell and Company

The first ever architectural application of Teflon-coated glass fibre in this country has worn well over its first seven years.

1 The hanging baskets and climbing plants have gone and Clifton Nurseries has become Judy's Pantry. The fabric roof, however, still looks good and performs well.

This little structure was built in 1982 on land belonging to the Royal Opera House in the north-east corner of Covent Garden. Plans for the long-term use of the land were uncertain, so it was let on a short lease to Clifton Nurseries for use as a retail outlet on the understanding that the site would be revitalised and the surroundings landscaped. This was designed, therefore, as a temporary building. Seven years later it is still in use, though not as a garden shop but as a café.

The most interesting feature of the design is the use of Teflon-coated glass-fibre fabric. This was the first ever architectural use of the material in this country. It is used in two ways: as a roof and as a wall.

The roof is a single sheet of fabric, 0.5 mm thick, tailored from smaller panels cut to computer-generated shapes and joined by welded seams to create a double-curved profile. The fabric is tensioned by being stretched over the steel frame and pulled inwards by means of tension cables and plywood discs or 'buttons'. Edges are fixed by means of a 'luff groove' detail similar to that used for the sails of racing yachts.

Conversion into a café has involved the introduction of a suspended ceiling over most of the floor area, which destroys the pleasant diffused daylighting effect of the original. However, the roof still functions perfectly well. There are no leaks, and condensation does not appear to be a major problem,

though there are slight traces of fungal growth on the inside fabric surface.

The main problems occur around the plywood buttons:
● the marine plywood external discs are in poor condition and moss has grown in the external depressions they create. Plywood seems to have been a cheap alternative to metal for this component
● there has been no loss of tension (a slight wrinkling below the buttons was probably always present)
● the fabric is dirty, but uniformly so. Welded seams have collected much more dirt than the main areas of fabric, possibly because the surface is slightly roughened. Cleaning with mild detergent is all that is required
● there is no gutter, and rain-water drains from the roof between mild steel upstand plates over pressed-metal flashings. This arrangement seems to cause no problems
● the mastic sealant around the mild steel upstands is unsightly and seems crude in comparison with the other roof components.

When used as a wall the fabric is less successful, though again there seem to have been no major failures. The main problem is that when used as a flat surface, the fabric is more difficult to tension. There is much more slackness and wrinkling in the wall panels than in the roof. This is at its worst in the half-gable at the back of the building where the fabric has become very loose. ■

Acknowledgment
The editors acknowledge the help of John Pringle of Michael Hopkins and Partners in the preparation of this article.

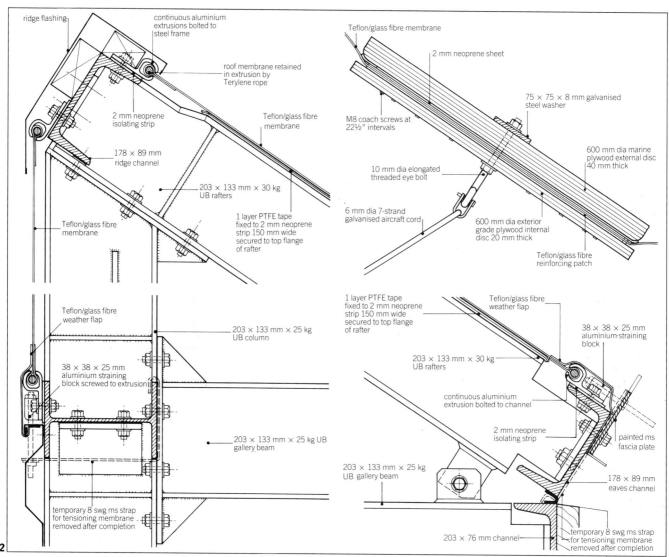

2

ridge flashing

continuous aluminium extrusions bolted to steel frame

roof membrane retained in extrusion by Terylene rope

2 mm neoprene isolating strip

178 × 89 mm ridge channel

Teflon/glass fibre membrane

203 × 133 mm × 30 kg UB rafters

Teflon/glass fibre membrane

1 layer PTFE tape fixed to 2 mm neoprene strip 150 mm wide secured to top flange of rafter

Teflon/glass fibre membrane

2 mm neoprene sheet

M8 coach screws at 22½° intervals

10 mm dia elongated threaded eye bolt

6 mm dia 7-strand galvanised aircraft cord

75 × 75 × 8 mm galvanised steel washer

600 mm dia marine plywood external disc 40 mm thick

600 mm dia exterior grade plywood internal disc 20 mm thick

Teflon/glass fibre reinforcing patch

Teflon/glass fibre weather flap

38 × 38 × 25 mm aluminium straining block screwed to extrusion

203 × 133 mm × 25 kg UB column

203 × 133 mm × 25 kg UB gallery beam

temporary 8 swg ms strap for tensioning membrane removed after completion

1 layer PTFE tape fixed to 2 mm neoprene strip 150 mm wide secured to top flange of rafter

Teflon/glass fibre weather flap

203 × 133 mm × 30 kg UB rafters

continuous aluminium extrusion bolted to channel

2 mm neoprene isolating strip

203 × 133 mm × 25 kg UB gallery beam

203 × 76 mm channel

38 × 38 × 25 mm aluminium straining block

painted ms fascia plate

178 × 89 mm eaves channel

temporary 8 swg ms strap for tensioning membrane removed after completion

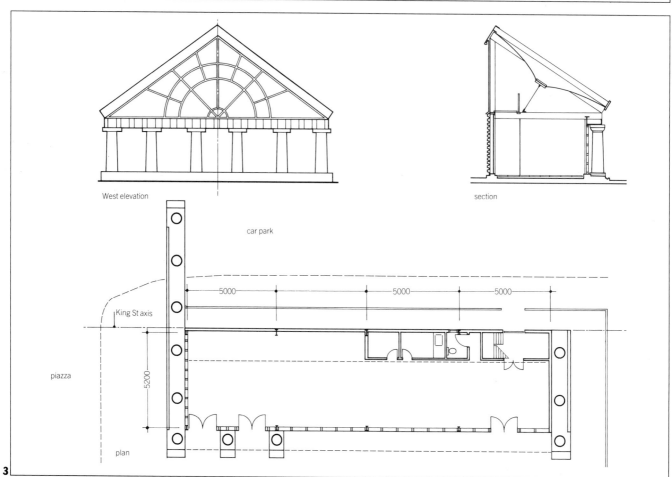

3

West elevation

section

car park

King St axis

5000   5000   5000

piazza

5200

plan

2 Sections through edges of wall and roof membranes, showing luff groove detail and temporary tensioning devices (dotted).
3 The pedimented facade and primitive Doric columns clothe an experimental high-technology structure.
4 Fabric wall panel with wrinkled corner. The double-curved and tensioned roof panels are more successful.
5 Plywood 'button' from the inside showing the shadow of moss growing in the roof depression.
6 Worm's eye view and bird's eye view showing the relationship between fabric membranes and steel frame.

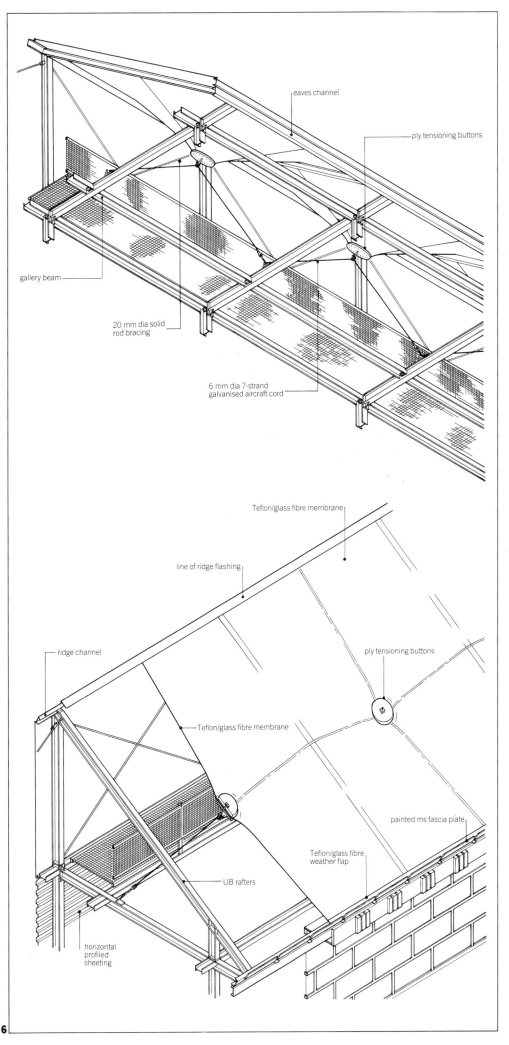

eaves channel

ply tensioning buttons

gallery beam

20 mm dia solid rod bracing

6 mm dia 7-strand galvanised aircraft cord

Teflon/glass fibre membrane

line of ridge flashing

ridge channel

ply tensioning buttons

Teflon/glass fibre membrane

painted ms fascia plate

Teflon/glass fibre weather flap

UB rafters

horizontal profiled sheeting

6

Credits
location Covent Garden, London
client Clifton Nurseries
contractor Wiltshier Construction
architects Terry Farrell and Company
structural engineers Ove Arup and Partners
Teflon-coated glass fibre Fothergill and Harvey

TEMPORARY STRUCTURE
EXHIBITION BUILDING
Terry Farrell and Company

Teflon-coated glass fibre is not the only material suitable for fabric structures. The Alexandra Pavilion used a cheaper alternative: PVC-coated polyester.

1

1 The fabric is dirty and damaged but the building has served its purpose well. It is now to be sold for re-erection elsewhere. Note the aluminium luff groove extrusions bolted to the flanges of the steel portal frames.

Acknowledgment
The editors acknowledge the help of Brian Foster of Ove Arup and Partners in the preparation of this article.

When Alexandra Palace was gutted by fire in 1980 its owners decided to build a temporary structure to house exhibitions, conferences, concerts and sports events until the main building was rebuilt. The Alexandra Pavilion, now seven years old, has served its purpose well. The palace is once again in use as an exhibition hall and the pavilion is to be sold for re-erection elsewhere.

This was one of the pioneer fabric structures in this country, along with the Clifton Nurseries building in Covent Garden (AJ 1.2.89 p49). But whereas Clifton Nurseries was a one-off, experimental building using Teflon-coated glass fibre, the Alexandra Pavilion was an adapted version of a standard design using the much cheaper PVC-coated polyester. In its standard form the design developed by Shelter-Span consisted of portal frames of extruded aluminium incorporating 'luff grooves' to hold the fabric. However, the 36-metre span of the Alexandra Pavilion was too great for aluminium, and steel was substituted, with additional aluminium extrusions bolted on. There are two such extrusions, on the top and bottom flanges of the frames, holding two fabric membranes.

The building has already survived beyond its intended life-span and is in reasonably good condition. However:
● there are signs that the PVC coating to the fabric is beginning to deteriorate and there is some loss of plasticiser on the west side, which is the side that is most exposed to the sun
● PVC does not have Teflon's self-cleaning properties and the fabric is now very dirty
● the luff groove detail is neat and elegant, but not always waterproof. In certain conditions the flow of rain-water down the shallow pitch of the roof spills over into the luff grooves. The inner fabric membrane acts as a second line of defence
● in a few places the outer membrane has torn and the welded seams of the inner membrane have parted, but these isolated failures seem to be due to accidental damage rather than inherent weakness.

Whereas the luff groove detail is derived from racing-yacht technology, fixings at the top and bottom of the long fabric panels owe more to covered lorries. The bottom edge of the panel is wrapped around a square hollow section purlin and continuously welded. Top edges are secured to purlins and tensioned by means of heavy-duty ratchet straps. At the junction of the main roof and the lower 'lean-to' roofs the layers of fabric are interleaved and laced together.

At the time the pavilion was built the fashion in permanent exhibition buildings was for 'black boxes', completely artificially lit. However, the daylit interior of the pavilion was well liked by exhibitors and this had some influence on the design of the rebuilt main exhibition hall, which is daylit and which also incorporates translucent fabric structures. ■

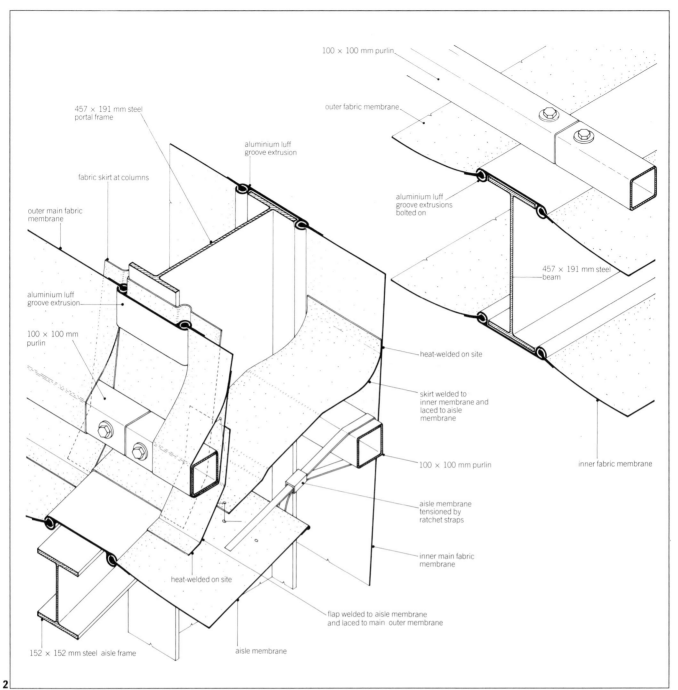

100 × 100 mm purlin

outer fabric membrane

aluminium luff groove extrusions bolted on

457 × 191 mm steel beam

inner fabric membrane

457 × 191 mm steel portal frame

aluminium luff groove extrusion

fabric skirt at columns

outer main fabric membrane

aluminium luff groove extrusion

100 × 100 mm purlin

heat-welded on site

skirt welded to inner membrane and laced to aisle membrane

100 × 100 mm purlin

aisle membrane tensioned by ratchet straps

inner main fabric membrane

heat-welded on site

flap welded to aisle membrane and laced to main outer membrane

152 × 152 mm steel aisle frame

aisle membrane

2

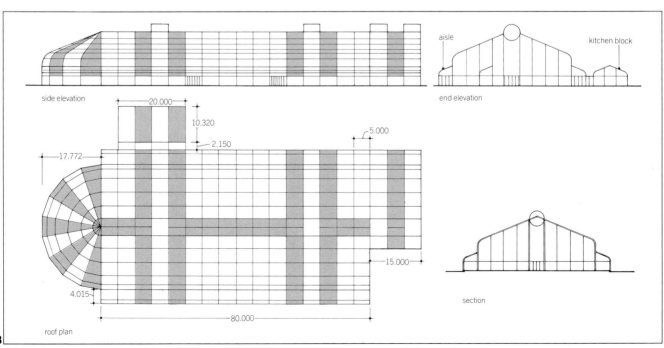

side elevation

aisle

kitchen block

end elevation

20.000

10.320

2.150

5.000

17.772

15.000

4.015

80.000

section

roof plan

3

4

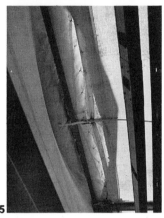

5

2 Cut-away isometric drawings. Left: junction of aisle and main roofs showing fabric retention details. Right: typical section through portal frame showing luff groove extrusions to retain the inner and outer membranes of the main roof.
3 General arrangement drawings.
4 Fabric panels are cut and welded to form a double-curved surface. Exposed steel purlins are galvanised.
5 Looking up at the internal junction of aisle and main roofs. The curved surface to the left is the lower part of the inner membrane of the main roof.
6 Cut-away axonometric drawing and detail location.

Credits
location Alexandra Palace, London
client Alexandra Palace
Development Team
planning architect Dr Peter Smith
consultant architects Terry Farrell
and Company
structural engineer Peter Rice, with
Ian Ritchie of Chrysalis Architects
mechanical and electrical engineers
Ronald Hurst Associates
contractor Henry Boot Construction
principal subcontractor Shelter-Span

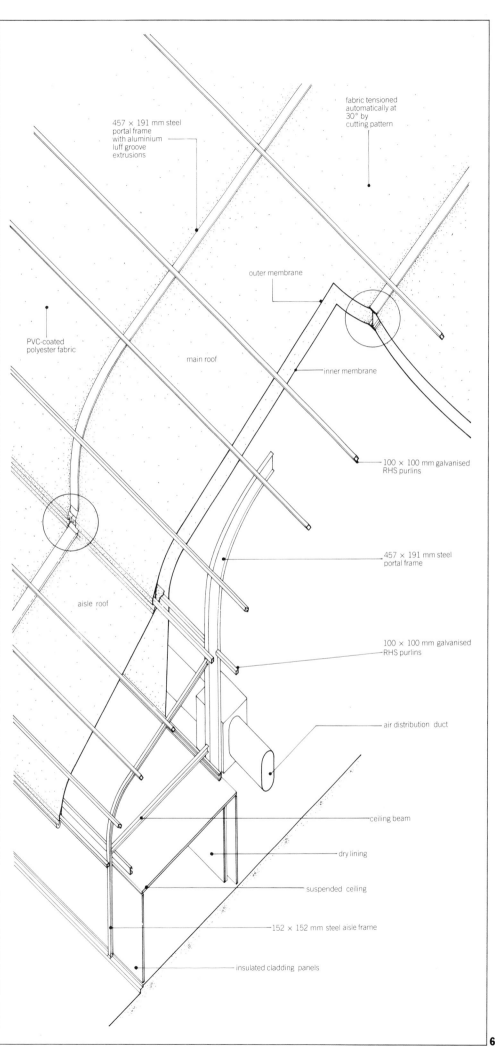

457 × 191 mm steel portal frame with aluminium luff groove extrusions

fabric tensioned automatically at 30° by cutting pattern

outer membrane

main roof

PVC-coated polyester fabric

inner membrane

100 × 100 mm galvanised RHS purlins

457 × 191 mm steel portal frame

aisle roof

100 × 100 mm galvanised RHS purlins

air distribution duct

ceiling beam

dry lining

suspended ceiling

152 × 152 mm steel aisle frame

insulated cladding panels

6

CANOPY STRUCTURE
TÊTE DÉFENSE CUBE
J. O. Spreckelsen

The 'cloud' at Tête Défense is a structure within a structure. It was intended that it should appear to float over the base of the 'Grand Arche' (the hollowed-out 'Cube'), providing shelter and human scale.

1 Looking down on the cloud. It is visible from all directions so no part of the construction can be hidden from view.

The 'cloud' at the base of the grand archway in the Cube building at Tête Défense was an essential part of architect J. O. Spreckelsen's competition-winning design.

It was to provide a living contrast to the clean geometry of the Cube, to introduce human scale, and to allow shelter and a wind-break in a space that would create its own microclimate.

As the detail design evolved it became evident that the original concept, of glass plates supported on a tension-braced steel space frame, would be difficult to achieve on both practical and cost grounds, so Spreckelsen himself, now working with Paul Andreu of Aéroports de Paris, was involved in the decision to look for an alternative way of creating the cloud. When Spreckelsen resigned from the project the concept of the canvas membrane structure was already well developed. Peter Rice was commissioned specifically to work on the design of the cloud.

The structure required to represent the lightness and spontaneity of a cloud, but it also had the constraints of fitting around the freestanding lift tower, withstanding the wind-loading and complying with the fire regulations. In addition, construction of the Cube had already started before the detailed design of the cloud was complete, so there were already limits on the position and capacity of anchorages for the canopy construction.

The plateau between the two built-up sides of the Cube is a fire-escape route and the building is divided into single-storey fire compartments, so the cloud was designed to retain its structural integrity even if it should lose all the cable supports from within any individual compartment.

The design which resulted ranges in height from 9 m to 25 m above the plateau, and the canopy covers an area of about 2000 m^2.

The tensioned structure spanning between the two sides of the Cube is formed from convex-shaped cable beams pre-stressed against 'free-form' edge cables. The supports are locked-coil and spiral strand cables which vary in diameter from 20 mm to 80 mm. Anchorage fittings and nodes were chosen to be freely rotating both during the life of the structure and during construction. Typical anchorage loads are much as 100 tonnes. Where necessary purpose-designed steel castings were used.

The canopy fabric is a 1 mm thick translucent PTFE-coated woven textile membrane which is stressed against the underside of the cable beams. A series of transparent 1 m diameter glass discs, supported from beneath by small flying struts, punctuate the warped surface of the canopy.

As anticipated, the initial buff colour of the canopy is bleaching to a pure white after exposure to sunlight. ∎

Acknowledgment
The editors acknowledge the help of Brian Forster of Ove Arup & Partners in the preparation of this article.

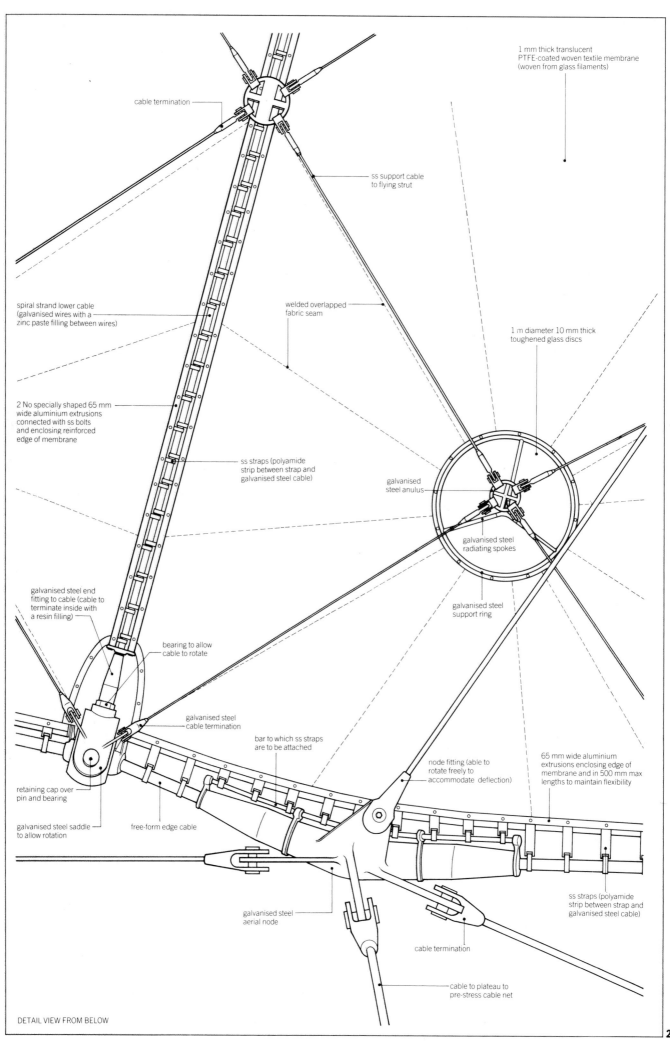

1 mm thick translucent
PTFE-coated woven textile membrane
(woven from glass filaments)

cable termination

ss support cable
to flying strut

spiral strand lower cable
(galvanised wires with a
zinc paste filling between wires)

welded overlapped
fabric seam

1 m diameter 10 mm thick
toughened glass discs

2 No specially shaped 65 mm
wide aluminium extrusions
connected with ss bolts
and enclosing reinforced
edge of membrane

ss straps (polyamide
strip between strap and
galvanised steel cable)

galvanised
steel anulus

galvanised steel
radiating spokes

galvanised steel
support ring

galvanised steel end
fitting to cable (cable to
terminate inside with
a resin filling)

bearing to allow
cable to rotate

galvanised steel
cable termination

bar to which ss straps
are to be attached

node fitting (able to
rotate freely to
accommodate deflection)

65 mm wide aluminium
extrusions enclosing edge of
membrane and in 500 mm max
lengths to maintain flexibility

retaining cap over
pin and bearing

free-form edge cable

galvanised steel saddle
to allow rotation

ss straps (polyamide
strip between strap and
galvanised steel cable)

galvanised steel
aerial node

cable termination

cable to plateau to
pre-stress cable net

DETAIL VIEW FROM BELOW

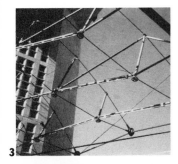

3

4

2 Detail view of the cloud from below. The cables to the plateau at the foot of the drawing are 76 mm in diameter.
3, 4 Photographs of the cloud taken during construction.
5 West elevation and plan showing the cloud structure without the fabric membrane.

Credits
location Route de la Demi-lune, La Défense, Paris, France
client SAEM (Société Anonyme d'Economie Mixte Nationale)
architect (responsible for the prize-winning design) J.O. Spreckelsen
architect Aéroports de Paris
architect (maitrise d'oeuvre) Paul Andreu
consultant engineer (maitrise d'oeuvre) RFR: Peter Rice, SARL
specialist engineer Ove Arup and Partners International Ltd
main contractor Bouygues SA
steel contractor Viry SA
fabric contractor Koitwerk GmbH and Co
cable supplier Pfeifer, Seil and Hebetechnik and Co
membrane technology Hoechst and Verseidag

Photo credit
Photograph 1 by Martin Charles.
Photographs 2 and 3 by RFR.

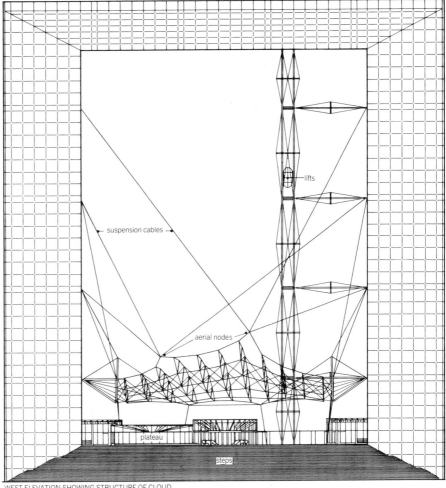

WEST ELEVATION SHOWING STRUCTURE OF CLOUD

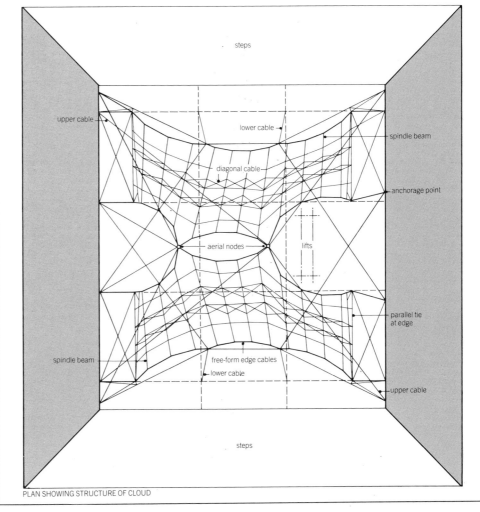

PLAN SHOWING STRUCTURE OF CLOUD

5

BALCONIES
PRIVATE HOUSING
Richard Rogers and Partners

Lightweight tubular steel-framed balconies are located between the three brick and glass fronted housing blocks that line the River Thames at Hammersmith.

1

1 The balconies project out over the river walk to allow panoramic views upstream and downstream.

Acknowledgment
The editors acknowledge the help of John Campbell of Farrell and Company, and Lionel Friedland of Pentarch in the preparation of this article.

The balconies between blocks are shared by two neighbouring flats. They are placed to the side of each living room rather than in front to allow each room an uninterrupted view of the water. Access is via side doors in the curtain walling system.

The lightweight steel structures are supported on a 219 mm dia CHS main pivot beam that sits on bearing brackets bolted back to the reinforced concrete floor slabs. To prevent the rigid platform rotating on the pivot beam, the whole structure is tied back to the adjoining buildings with steel tension rods. The paired central lattice beams at right angles to the pivot beam are further stiffened by pairs of tie-rods fixed to a central CHS post projecting above and below the pivot beam. Tapering lattice beams, at right angles to the central lattice beam at 1400 mm centres, connect to a shallow tubular ladder beam at the platform edge.

The Iroko timber decking is laid to falls to a central stainless steel drainage channel between the lattice beams. Rain-water drains from deck to deck, down stainless steel chains, to drains at ground level. The decking has a routed and lapped movement joint between each plank and two grooves on the top surface of each plank. These joints and grooves are intended to channel water off the deck, prevent water from seeping into the terrace below and provide a slip-resistant surface.

Balustrading consists of tubular steel posts and horizontal rails with the handrail projecting inwards to deter small children from climbing to the top. Balconies are subdivided by tensioned sailcloth panels spanning between the balustrading and the central CHS posts.

Further detailed considerations include:
● all structural fixing plates and bolts behind the face of the brickwork are of stainless steel. All maintainable (painted) structure is of tubular mild steel
● steelwork paint specification is as follows; gritblast, aluminium metal spray, two pack etch prime, one coat zinc phosphate, chlorinated rubber alkyd, chlorinated rubber undercoat, white alkyd top coat. Paint finish is intended to give three years to first maintenance, as stipulated by the leases
● under storm conditions the balcony chain-drain system could prove inadequate, leading to splashing of decking and brickwork by wind-blown rain-water
● the routed and lapped plank edge detail assists rain-water run-off but potentially weakens the boards, increasing the risk of cracking under point loading from chair legs, etc. Quarter-sawn timber was specified to avoid this problem.

The balconies were fabricated in two halves for ease of transport and bolted together on site through plates on either side of the pivot beam. Steelwork was factory-painted and touched up on site after assembly. ■

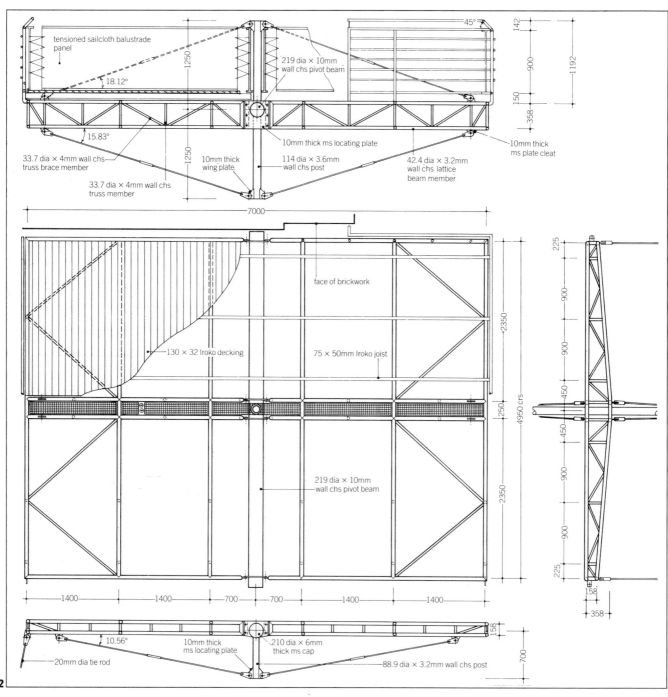

tensioned sailcloth balustrade panel

18.12°

1250

45°

142

900

1192

150

358

219 dia × 10mm wall chs pivot beam

10mm thick ms plate cleat

15.83°

10mm thick ms locating plate

33.7 dia × 4mm wall chs truss brace member

1250

10mm thick wing plate

114 dia × 3.6mm wall chs post

42.4 dia × 3.2mm wall chs lattice beam member

33.7 dia × 4mm wall chs truss member

7000

225

face of brickwork

900

2350

130 × 32 Iroko decking

75 × 50mm Iroko joist

450

250

450

219 dia × 10mm wall chs pivot beam

2350

900

4950 crs

225

158

1400   1400   700   700   1400   1400

358

10.56°

10mm thick ms locating plate

210 dia × 6mm thick ms cap

158

700

20mm dia tie rod

88.9 dia × 3.2mm wall chs post

2

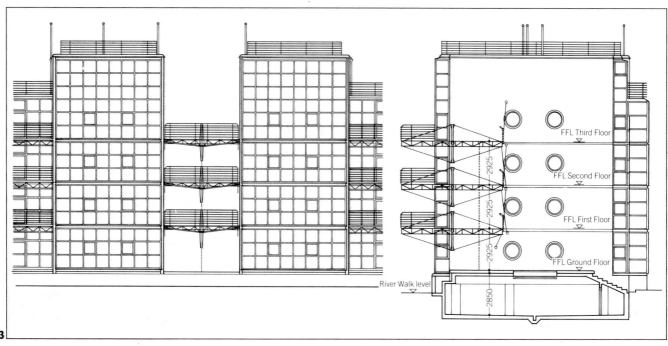

FFL Third Floor

2925

FFL Second Floor

2925

FFL First Floor

2925

FFL Ground Floor

River Walk level

2850

3

2 Plan and elevations of balcony structure.
3 Section and partial riverside elevation of the housing blocks, showing balcony location.
4 Balconies are subdivided by tensioned sailcloth panels.
5 Paired central lattice beams are stiffened by pairs of tie-rods fixed to a central CHS post that projects above and below the pivot beam.
6 Isometric details at the central drainage channel, top, and landward balustrade, below.

Credits
location Rainville Road, London W6
client Croudace Construction
architect Richard Rogers and Partners: Peter Angrave (project architect), Paul Cook, Ian Gibson, Marco Goldschmied, Sarah Grenville, Ian Hopton, Tim Inskip, Janette Mackie, Mark Roche, Richard Rogers, John Young
quantity surveyor Melvyn Newell
mechanical and electrical engineers The Sinnett Partnership
structural engineer Hay Barry & Partners
landscape architects Rendel & Branch
main contractor Croudace Construction
steel balconies and balustrading Nusteel Structures
timber decking Wenban-Smith Joinery
marine fittings to balustrades Barlow Gibbs UK
ss rain-water goods Component Developments
sailcloth terrace subdivisions North Sails (UK)

Photo credit
Photographs by Padraig Boyle.

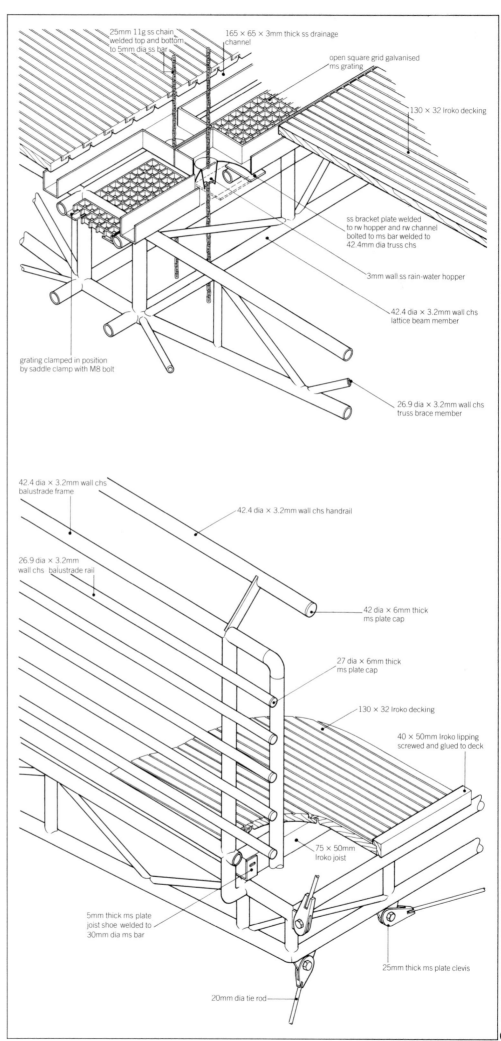

25mm 11g ss chain welded top and bottom to 5mm dia ss bar

165 × 65 × 3mm thick ss drainage channel

open square grid galvanised ms grating

130 × 32 Iroko decking

ss bracket plate welded to rw hopper and rw channel bolted to ms bar welded to 42.4mm dia truss chs

3mm wall ss rain-water hopper

42.4 dia × 3.2mm wall chs lattice beam member

26.9 dia × 3.2mm wall chs truss brace member

grating clamped in position by saddle clamp with M8 bolt

42.4 dia × 3.2mm wall chs balustrade frame

42.4 dia × 3.2mm wall chs handrail

26.9 dia × 3.2mm wall chs balustrade rail

42 dia × 6mm thick ms plate cap

27 dia × 6mm thick ms plate cap

130 × 32 Iroko decking

40 × 50mm Iroko lipping screwed and glued to deck

75 × 50mm Iroko joist

5mm thick ms plate joist shoe welded to 30mm dia ms bar

25mm thick ms plate clevis

20mm dia tie rod

6

BALCONIES
PRIVATE HOUSE
David Wild

This house for a private client has white GRC-rendered walls and steel-framed balconies with timber duckboarding.

1

1 The new house at No 42 Rochester Place, right, occupies the site next to David Wild's own house which he completed in 1984.

Acknowledgment
The editors acknowledge the help of John Campbell of Terry Farrell and Company and Lionel Friedland of Pentarch in the preparation of this article.

On the strength of the commission for this house, and in the light of experience gained in building his own house (AJ 20.3.85 p42) on the neighbouring site, David Wild set up a design and build company to execute the work. The budget was tight which meant that the site work-force was small and specialised, with Wild himself contributing much of the labour.

External walls and structure to first-floor level are of 'heavy' construction, with a lightweight mezzanine and roof. The first floor, consisting of 150 mm thick precast concrete planks grouted together, is supported on an exposed frame of fairfaced in-situ concrete. A central circular concrete column rises through the double-height first-floor living space to support the metal roof trusses.

The walls are of highly insulative concrete blocks; 100 mm outer leaf, 190 mm inner leaf, with a 50 mm cavity. The external finish is 10 mm thick, white, self-coloured GRC render. This is applied in one coat and does not shrink or crack. Internally the walls are lined with 25 mm foam-backed plasterboard on dabs, with taped and filled joints. This enhances the insulative performance of the walls to give a U-value of $0.3W/m^2°C$, and provides a convenient 'duct' space for running cables. It also eliminated an expensive and time-consuming craft skill from the site operation. A suspended plasterboard ceiling system was used above the large first-floor

living space, to achieve an accuracy of line and an evenness of plane that would not have been possible with a skim finish.

The cold roof construction comprises lead-coated stainless steel sheet with standing seams and ventilating cowls, on felt underlay, over 18 mm exterior grade plywood sheathing. This is supported on Z-purlins spanning between the eight radially organised roof trusses. The roof sheet is dressed down into a preformed zinc gutter with welded seams, which also acts as a coping to the rendered walls.

Further detailed considerations include:
● the Metsec roof trusses are anchored to padstones on the inner, loadbearing, blockwork skin and bolted together by a central flanged steel collar that locates over a 25 mm dia steel rod cast into the rc column
● balconies on the front and garden facades have painted galvanised ms channel frames with stained hardwood duckboard infill. Balustrading on the larger, garden balcony is of 25 mm square grid galvanised mesh in a 25 mm dia welded CHS frame
● the W20 metal-framed windows are only single-glazed but heat loss is offset by the highly insulated walls. Condensation is a potential problem but is a calculated risk; specifying a double-glazed system would have introduced thicker and visually obtrusive glazing bars and would have been prohibitively expensive. ■

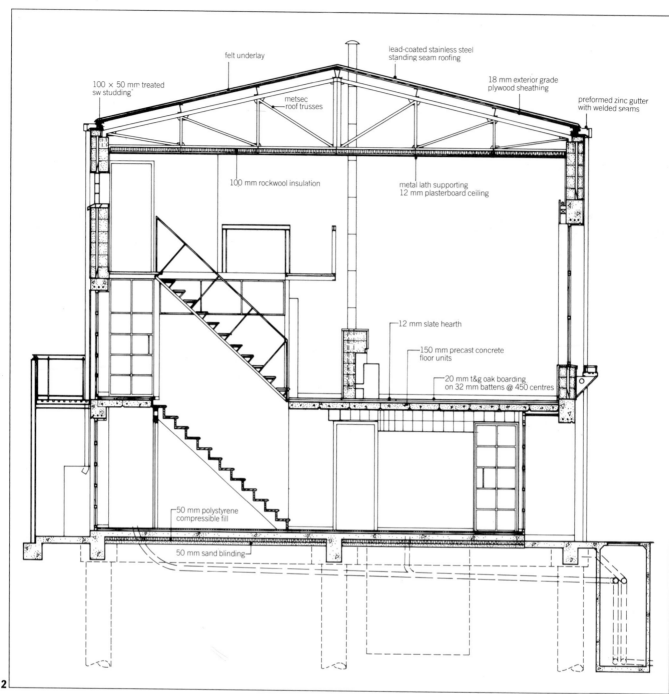

2

felt underlay

lead-coated stainless steel
standing seam roofing

100 × 50 mm treated
sw studding

18 mm exterior grade
plywood sheathing

metsec
roof trusses

preformed zinc gutter
with welded seams

100 mm rockwool insulation

metal lath supporting
12 mm plasterboard ceiling

12 mm slate hearth

150 mm precast concrete
floor units

20 mm t&g oak boarding
on 32 mm battens @ 450 centres

50 mm polystyrene
compressible fill

50 mm sand blinding

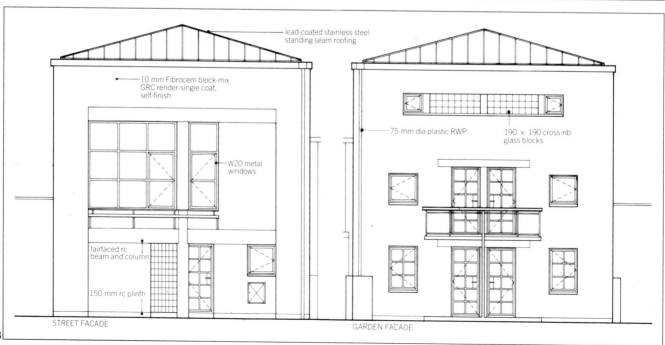

3

lead-coated stainless steel
standing seam roofing

10 mm Fibrocem block-mix
GRC render-single coat,
self-finish

75 mm dia plastic RWP

190 × 190 cross-rib
glass blocks

W20 metal
windows

fairfaced rc
beam and column

150 mm rc plinth

STREET FACADE

GARDEN FACADE

2 Detailed cross-section. The living area, located on the first floor, is a double-height space, with a lightweight metal structure mezzanine.
3 Street facade, left, and garden facade, right.
4 The garden facade.
5 Detail of balcony on street facade.
6 Isometric drawing of balcony on the garden facade.
7 Isometric drawing of balcony on the street facade, located below the large living-room windows.

Credits
location 42 Rochester Place, London NW1
architect David Wild
engineer John Romer
contractor David Wild Design and Build (DWDB)
block layer Ken Crawford
joinery Andrew Crawford
building team Andrew Brook, Neil Manley, Ian Fairweather, Mark Goldspink and Louise James
piling Colets Earth Boring
rendering Grant & Harrington
metal windows Senlac Metal Casements
metalwork Holborn Metalworks
blockwork Thermalite
precast floor units Durox
granite and marble work Diespeker
plastering Internal Linings
oak and cedar supplier Acorn Hardwoods
roofing, gutters BIZ
roof trusses Metsec

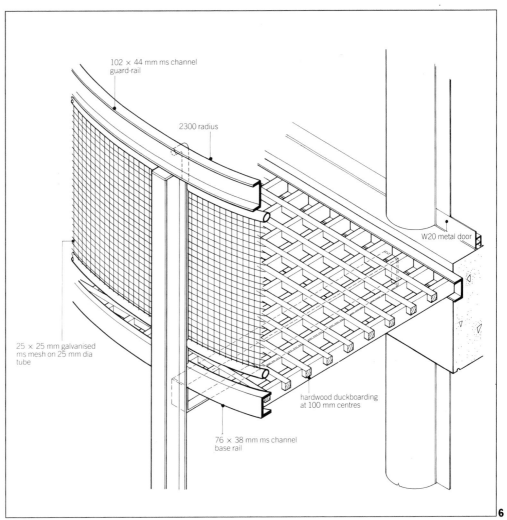

102 × 44 mm ms channel guard-rail

2300 radius

W20 metal door

25 × 25 mm galvanised ms mesh on 25 mm dia tube

hardwood duckboarding at 100 mm centres

76 × 38 mm ms channel base rail

6

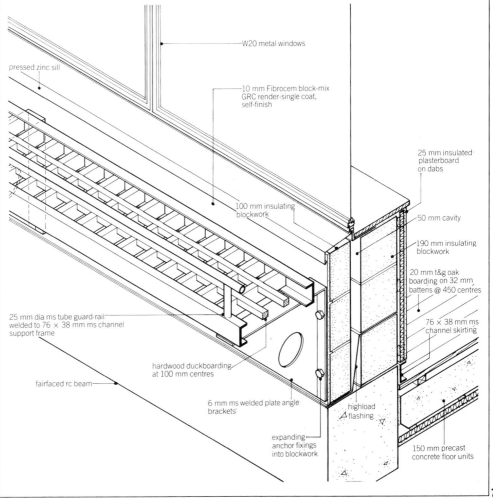

W20 metal windows

pressed zinc sill

10 mm Fibrocem block-mix GRC render-single coat, self-finish

25 mm insulated plasterboard on dabs

50 mm cavity

100 mm insulating blockwork

190 mm insulating blockwork

20 mm t&g oak boarding on 32 mm battens @ 450 centres

76 × 38 mm ms channel skirting

25 mm dia ms tube guard-rail welded to 76 × 38 mm ms channel support frame

hardwood duckboarding at 100 mm centres

fairfaced rc beam

6 mm ms welded plate angle brackets

highload flashing

expanding anchor fixings into blockwork

150 mm precast concrete floor units

7

BALCONY
RESIDENTIAL BUILDING
Elder & Cannon

This balcony, embedded in an attic storey, is an exercise in the construction of stone copings and cornices. An apparently simple form conceals a complex structure of in-situ and precast concrete, rendered brickwork and steel.

1

1 The south-facing Wilson Street elevation, showing the projecting balcony at fifth-floor level. The only visible support to the balcony floor is a single precast concrete bracket.

Acknowledgment
The editors acknowledge the help of John Campbell of Terry Farrell and Company and Lionel Friedland of Pentarch in the preparation of this article.

This balcony is the central feature of the main elevation of a residential building at Ingram Square, Glasgow. The balcony is at fifth-floor level. A sixth floor, partly in the pitch of the roof, is not directly expressed on the facade, but the windows of the balcony light double-height living-spaces with galleries.

The building has a steel frame with in-situ concrete floors on profiled steel permanent shuttering. It is clad in brickwork, rendered on the top storey. The brickwork is supported on galvanised steel angles bolted to in-situ edge beams. Courses of notched 'pistol' bricks avoid wide joints at the angle supports.

There are precast concrete projecting string-courses at various levels. The string-course at fifth-floor level, which is coloured red and divides the fairfaced brickwork from the rendered brickwork, swells out in a bow shape in the middle of the facade to form the balcony floor or sill.

This is made entirely from precast concrete components. It projects approximately 450 mm beyond the main face of the brickwork at the widest point, where it is supported by a precast concrete bracket bolted back to an in-situ concrete upstand at the edge of the floor slab. The back of the sill is held down by bolts through the floor slab.

In the middle of the balcony the roof is supported by a circular section steel column similar to those which support the projecting turret on the corner of Wilson Street and Brunswick Street. This column has an intumescent coating for fire protection.

At the top of the facade, a decorative cornice, made up from two precast concrete courses with an area of rendered brickwork between, also swells out to form a canopy over the balcony. Above this there is yet another precast concrete structure—a 'flying' coping —projecting above the roof line. This is stabilised by steel props behind.

Buildability had a strong influence on the detailed design of this three-tier coping. On a constricted urban site there was no room to manoeuvre a heavy crane and therefore the maximum size and weight of the precast concrete units were limited. The architects were keen to maintain the same high-quality surface finish as the string-courses lower down. It was decided, therefore, to make only the visible front part of the cornices in precast and to cast the back portion in situ. The concrete mix and formwork lining were carefully matched to the precast.

The structure is therefore a mixture of precast concrete, in-situ concrete and rendered brickwork, all supported on a steel frame. The various components are held together with galvanised anchor rods, cast-in sockets, bolts and angle cleats.

The central post of the steel balustrade assembly is fixed down into the precast sill, and the curved top rail is fixed to the brickwork at each end. ■

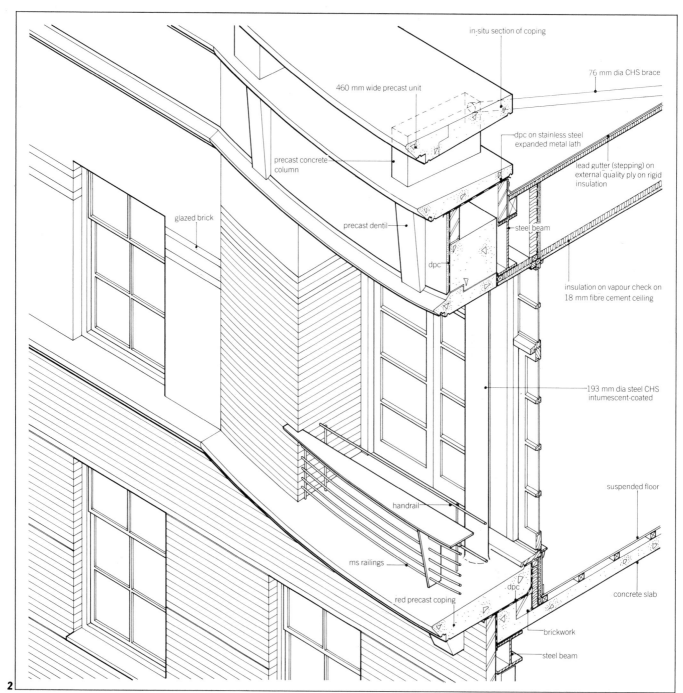

in-situ section of coping

76 mm dia CHS brace

460 mm wide precast unit

precast concrete column

dpc on stainless steel expanded metal lath

lead gutter (stepping) on external quality ply on rigid insulation

glazed brick

precast dentil

steel beam

dpc

insulation on vapour check on 18 mm fibre cement ceiling

193 mm dia steel CHS intumescent-coated

suspended floor

handrail

ms railings

dpc

concrete slab

red precast coping

brickwork

steel beam

2

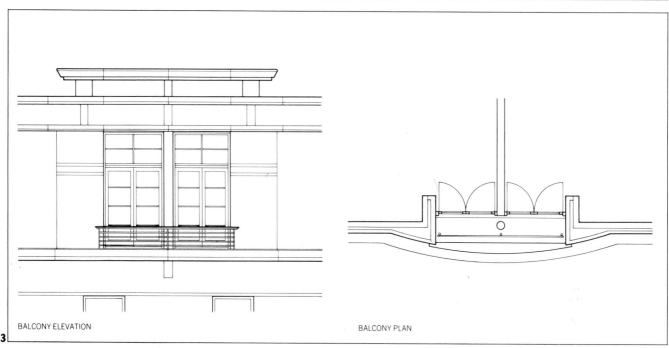

BALCONY ELEVATION

BALCONY PLAN

3

4

2 Cut-away isometric showing the structural supports for the balcony, and the cornice and coping above.
3 Balcony elevation and plan. The balcony windows light double-height living-spaces.
4 Close-up photograph of the balcony. Seen from this angle it is possible to identify the steel ties for the precast concrete columns which support the 'flying' coping.
5 Detail section through the balcony, showing the relationship of precast and in-situ concrete components.

Credits
location Ingram Square, Glasgow
clients Ingram Square Ltd (Kantel), Scottish Development Agency, Glasgow District Council
architect Elder & Cannon
quantity surveyor Tozer Gallagher and Partners
structural engineer Blyth and Blyth Partnership
main contractor Lawrence Construction
steel frame Bone Connell and Baxter
decorative metalwork Findlay Campbell
timber windows Hall and Tawse
render, partitions and roof Gypsum Construction
precast concrete Plean Precast

Photo credit
Alastair Hunter

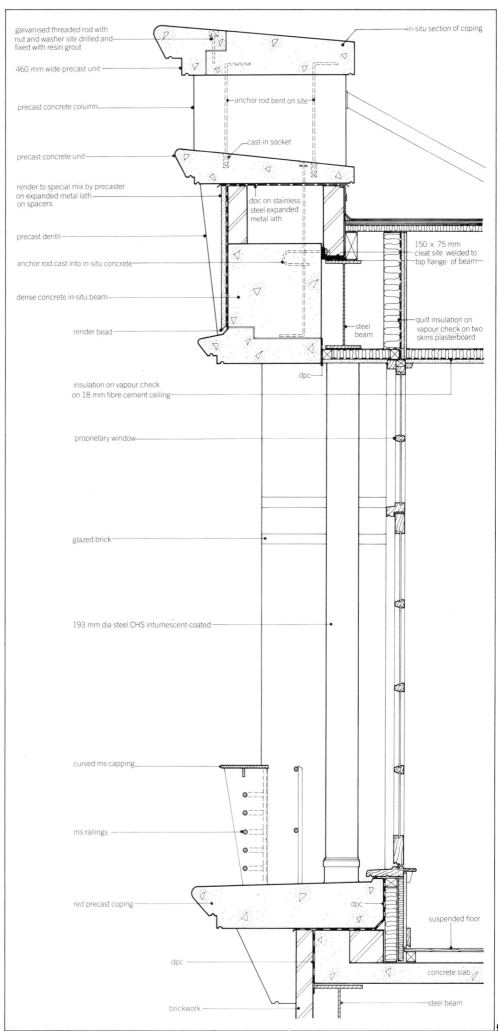

galvanised threaded rod with nut and washer site drilled and fixed with resin grout

in-situ section of coping

460 mm wide precast unit

anchor rod bent on site

precast concrete column

cast-in socket

precast concrete unit

render to special mix by precaster on expanded metal lath on spacers

dpc on stainless steel expanded metal lath

150 × 75 mm cleat site welded to top flange of beam

precast dentil

anchor rod cast into in-situ concrete

dense concrete in-situ beam

quilt insulation on vapour check on two skins plasterboard

render bead

steel beam

dpc

insulation on vapour check on 18 mm fibre cement ceiling

proprietary window

glazed brick

193 mm dia steel CHS intumescent-coated

curved ms capping

ms railings

red precast coping

dpc

suspended floor

dpc

concrete slab

brickwork

steel beam

5

METAL STAIRCASES
LEISURE POOL
Alsop and Lyall

Sheringham leisure pool has metal staircases, which offer a hard-edged counterpoint to the building's timber aesthetic.

1

1 The counterbalanced steel staircase leading to the flume slide platform can be lifted into a horizontal position to free the poolside for competition events.

The Sheringham pool is designed to be used for both leisure and competitive swimming.

Along one end of the pool, three steel staircases lead to steel-decked viewing platforms that cantilever over the water. One platform is used by the lifeguard for supervising the entire pool area.

A separate splash pool is provided at the end of a spiralling glassfibre flume slide. The slide sits on a tubular steel beam and is supported by radiating arms cantilevered from two central 'maypoles', one of which is suspended above the water and is supported by cross members at the end of an 8 m cantilever structure that projects through the plant room wall.

The flume slide platform is reached by two flights of steel stairs. The upper flight is fixed. The lower flight is counterbalanced and can be lifted into a horizontal position to cut off access to the flume and enable the regulation 2 m of space to be provided at the deep end poolside for competitive events. When down, the staircase is secured by a captive stainless steel anchor bolt into a threaded socket in the floor.

The staircases are designed as integral structures; strings, balustrading, treads and risers are all weld jointed. Welds were ground and polished smooth. Balustrade infill panels are of mild steel welded wire mesh on a mild steel frame. Handrails and strings are of cold-drawn, seamless mild steel tube. Treads

and risers are of mild steel tread plate covered with Altro non-slip flooring.

The three viewing platforms were designed originally as balanced structures with twin flights of stairs. This was changed to a single flight because the splash pool had to be a minimum size, which left no room for the second flight of the platform nearest to it. Platforms are supported on one steel leg located in the centre of the trellis columns. Viewing decks wrap around the trellis columns but do not touch them. Stair strings are of unequal size to take account of the differing torsional forces.

Other detailed considerations include:
● staircases are made from ungalvanised mild steel. Metalwork was factory prepared and painted; scratches were attended to on site.
● the paint specification is designed for maximum durability and protection; metal work was shotblasted, followed by one coat silicate zinc dust primer; one coat, two-pack epoxy micacious iron oxide, and finished with one coat routile titanium dioxide white epoxy.

In this case, stainless steel would have been a more suitable material than mild steel but was ruled out on grounds of expense. Maintenance will need to be of a high standard and any surface damage immediately touched up to prevent rust attack occurring due to the chemically hostile and humid swimming pool environment. ∎

Acknowledgement
The editors acknowledge the help of John Campbell and Lionel Friedland of Terry Farrell Partnership and formerly of Bickerdike Allen Partners, in the preparation of this article.

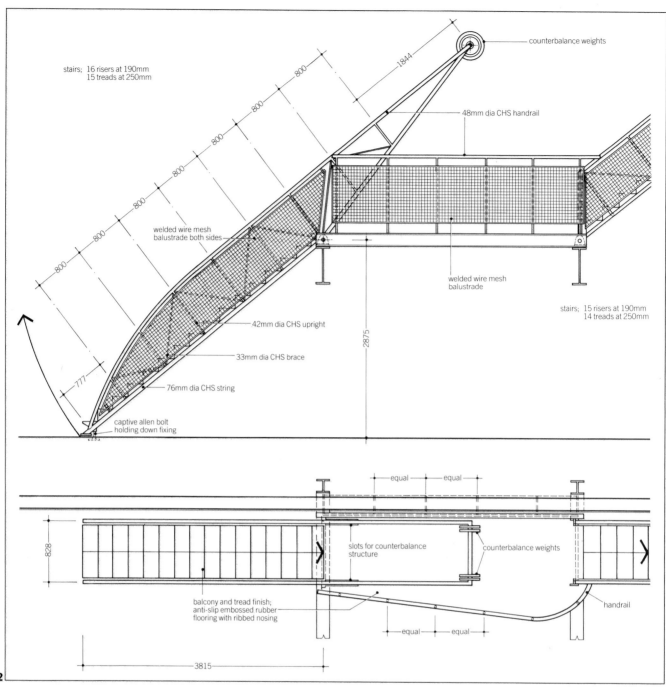

stairs; 16 risers at 190mm
15 treads at 250mm

counterbalance weights

1844

48mm dia CHS handrail

800
800
800
800
800
800
800
800

welded wire mesh
balustrade both sides

welded wire mesh
balustrade

2875

stairs; 15 risers at 190mm
14 treads at 250mm

42mm dia CHS upright

33mm dia CHS brace

76mm dia CHS string

777

captive allen bolt
holding down fixing

equal — equal

slots for counterbalance
structure

counterbalance weights

828

handrail

balcony and tread finish;
anti-slip embossed rubber
flooring with ribbed nosing

equal — equal

3815

2

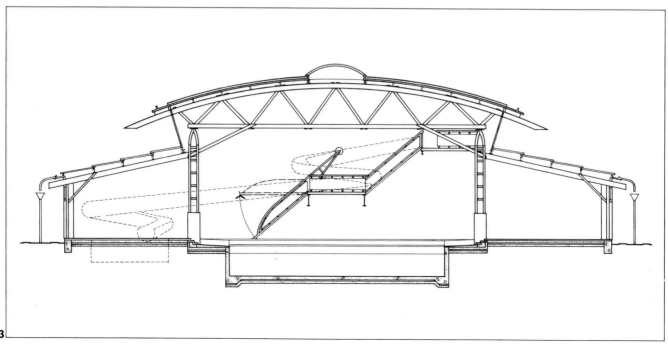

3

2 Plan and elevation of the flume staircase.
3 Cross section through the building showing location of flume and access staircase.
4 One of the three viewing platforms that are ranged along one side of the pool. The steel platforms are supported on a single leg located in the centre of the timber trellis columns. Stair strings are RSC sections of unequal size to take account of the different torsional forces.
5 Isometric details of the flume staircase. Top, detail at the pivot; centre, typical detail of treads and supporting brackets; bottom, detail at first tread, cut away to show anchorage point.

Credits
location Sheringham, Norfolk
client Clifford Barnett Group for Norfolk District Council
architects William Alsop and John Lyall
project architect Peter Clash
assistant architects Mike Waddington, Simon North, Jonathan Adams, Isabelle Lousada
quantity surveyor Drysdale de Leeuw and Partners
structural engineer Anthony Hunt Associates
management contractor Clugston Construction
metalwork and steelwork R. H. Howlett Engineering
flume slide Stuart Leisure

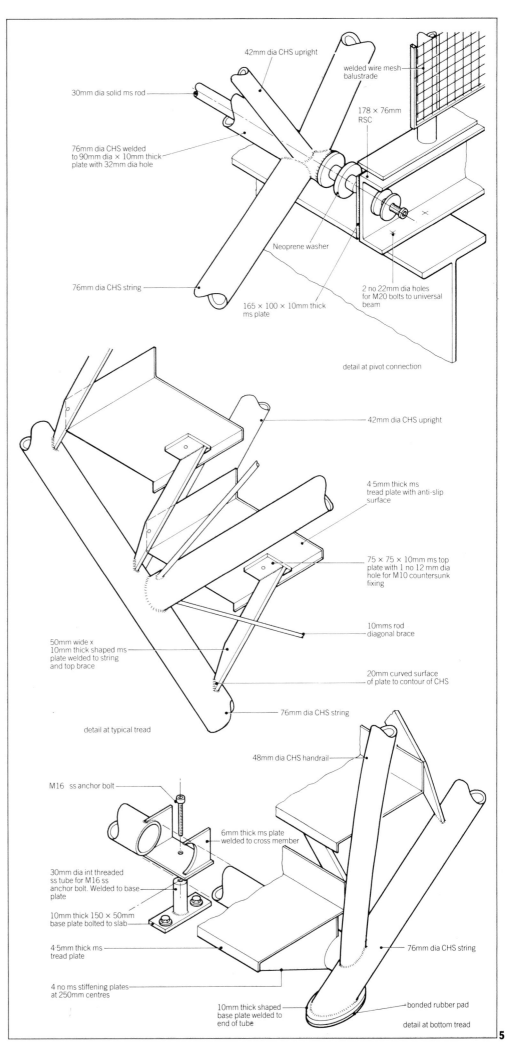

30mm dia solid ms rod

42mm dia CHS upright

welded wire mesh balustrade

178 × 76mm RSC

76mm dia CHS welded to 90mm dia × 10mm thick plate with 32mm dia hole

76mm dia CHS string

Neoprene washer

2 no 22mm dia holes for M20 bolts to universal beam

165 × 100 × 10mm thick ms plate

detail at pivot connection

42mm dia CHS upright

4·5mm thick ms tread plate with anti-slip surface

75 × 75 × 10mm ms top plate with 1 no 12 mm dia hole for M10 countersunk fixing

10mms rod diagonal brace

50mm wide x 10mm thick shaped ms plate welded to string and top brace

20mm curved surface of plate to contour of CHS

76mm dia CHS string

detail at typical tread

48mm dia CHS handrail

M16 ss anchor bolt

6mm thick ms plate welded to cross member

30mm dia int threaded ss tube for M16 ss anchor bolt. Welded to base plate

10mm thick 150 × 50mm base plate bolted to slab

4·5mm thick ms tread plate

76mm dia CHS string

4 no ms stiffening plates at 250mm centres

10mm thick shaped base plate welded to end of tube

bonded rubber pad

detail at bottom tread

CONCOURSE AND STAIRCASE
LAW COURTS
Evans and Shalev

Public circulation in the Truro Courts of Justice building is organised around a central concourse with brick-built staircases connecting the two levels.

1

1 The waiting area serving the Crown Courts is the largest of two circular double height spaces on the public circulation route. The colour scheme is predominantly black and white with planted greenery and bright red seating.

Acknowledgement
The editors acknowledge the help of Roland Gibbard of YRM Interiors in the preparation of this article.

The public concourse is essentially a linear route which connects two waiting spaces. The major space serves two Crown Courts, the minor serves a dual-purpose court. These circular spaces together form the organisational nodes for the building's public circulation system. The spaces are double height beneath conical roofed rotundas that dominate the skyline. They are day-lit by clerestory windows formed from glass blocks. Natural ventilation is provided by small opening lights between the large glass block panels.

Internal finishes continue the predominantly black and white aesthetic of the building's exterior. Bright red seating and planted greenery provide the colour highlights. Floors are finished with 200 x 200 mm white ceramic tiles over 100 mm screed. Square slate insets are placed at alternate tile corners, rather than at every corner, which increases the apparent scale of the floor pattern.

Walls and ceilings are plastered and finished with white emulsion paint. Doors are flush veneered with vision panels where necessary. Frames and profiled architraves are of softwood. Architraves and plastered walls are articulated by 12 mm shadow gaps. Skirtings are of profiled hardwood with similar shadow gaps. All woodwork is oil-painted white. Internal fixed windows are glazed with 6 mm Georgian wired clear glass in concealed steel

subframes set into hardwood frames.

Public staircases lead from the concourse to the first floor. One leads to the bailiff's office, cash office and waiting area, a second to the registrar's office and waiting area and a third to the jury accommodation.

The staircases are enclosed below string level by white plastered walls. Strings, treads and risers are made of blue/black Staffordshire bricks that are also used for low level walls and planters and as paving for the entrance circulation areas.

Stair treads and strings are articulated by narrow brick 'gutters' that follow the stringline along each side. Balustrading is of tubular steel with a white epoxy finish.

Further detailed considerations include:
● white walls and doors will require regular maintenance if the building is to retain its crisp appearance.
● ironmongery is robust and should last well, but door appearance could be improved by having fewer or smaller fixed plates
● seating in the waiting areas has supporting legs which do not hit the floor tile pattern consistently. A cantilevered seat bolted to the wall would have avoided this problem, but the location of radiators behind the seating precludes this option.

The materials used are predominantly traditional: bricks, plaster and tiles mixed with slate. Glass blocks are used extensively and provide a Modern counterpoint. ■

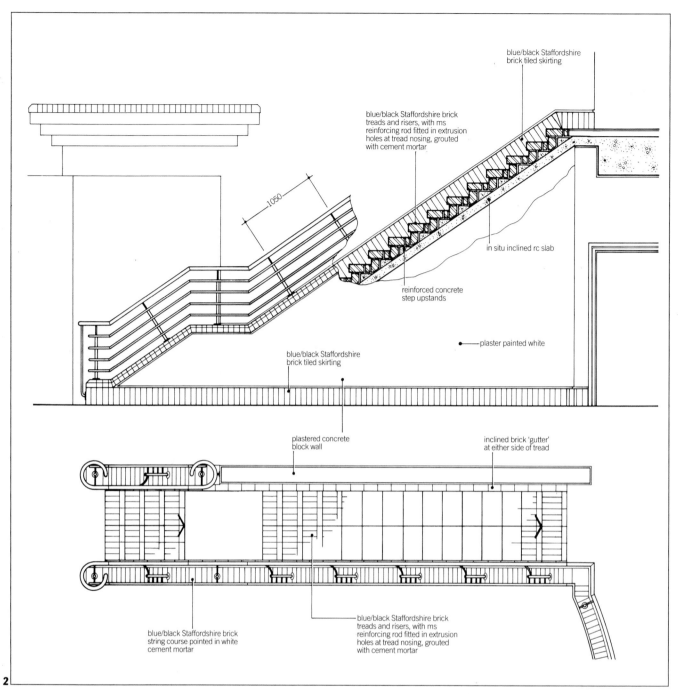

blue/black Staffordshire
brick tiled skirting

blue/black Staffordshire brick
treads and risers, with ms
reinforcing rod fitted in extrusion
holes at tread nosing, grouted
with cement mortar

1050

in situ inclined rc slab

reinforced concrete
step upstands

plaster painted white

blue/black Staffordshire
brick tiled skirting

plastered concrete
block wall

inclined brick 'gutter'
at either side of tread

blue/black Staffordshire brick
string course pointed in white
cement mortar

blue/black Staffordshire brick
treads and risers, with ms
reinforcing rod fitted in extrusion
holes at tread nosing, grouted
with cement mortar

2

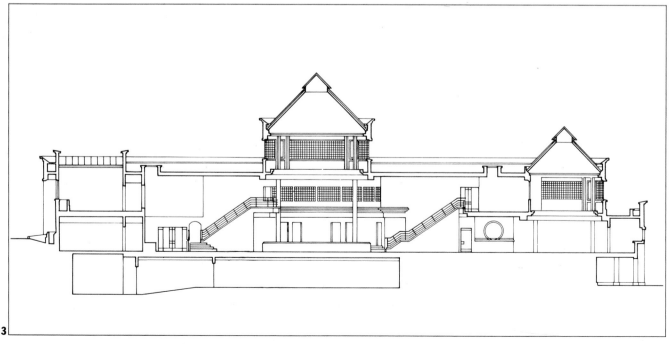

3

4

5

2 Plan and cut away elevation of the staircase that leads to the registrar's office and waiting room.
3 Section through the public circulation areas.
4 Detail of the tubular steel balustrade.
5 Photograph of stair taken during construction showing brick 'gutter' between treads and strings.
6 Balustrading is push-fit jointed at the upright and secured from underneath the tubes by grub screws. Uprights are bolted to concrete upstands. Coping bricks are cut to fit around the uprights.

Credits
location Edward Street, Truro
architects Evans and Shalev; Eldred Evans, David Shalev, Charles Mador
quantity surveyor MDA; Richard Pope, Kevin Heaton
structural engineer Anthony Hunt Associates; Stephen Morley, Alan Smith
services engineer Max Fordham and partners, Max Fordham, David Lindsay
contractor Dudley Coles Ltd
contract manager Bryan Hammond
site agent Tony Luke
clerk of works Wilf Ballm
project managers Property Services Agency, Martin Brooks, John Whiting, Jim Dunaway, Len Froom-Lewis
m & e subcontractors: mechanical installation Haden Young, Bristol *duct work,* Contract Air, *electrical installation* Staveley Industries *environmental controls* Satchwell Control System, *communication and fire alarms* Static Systems, *floor screeds and tiling* J.H. Lidstone *internal doors* H.C. Bridgman (Joinery), *louvred grilles* Waterloo Ozonair, *ceilings* Gary Richardson Ceilings, *glass block windows* Luxcrete *metal balustrading* T.C. Engineering *internal glazing* Andrewartha *ironmongery* James Gibbons Format *facing bricks* Hawkins Tiles (Cannock).

Photo credit
Photographs by Martin Charles

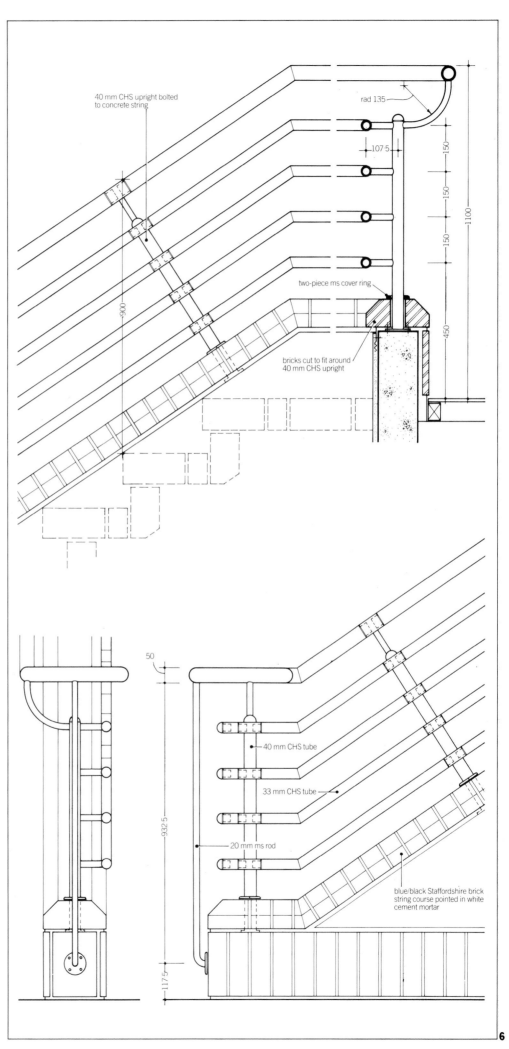

40 mm CHS upright bolted to concrete string

rad 135

107·5

150

150

1100

150

900

two-piece ms cover ring

450

bricks cut to fit around 40 mm CHS upright

50

40 mm CHS tube

33 mm CHS tube

20 mm ms rod

932·5

117·5

blue/black Staffordshire brick string course pointed in white cement mortar

6

STEEL STAIRCASE
SCHOOL OF ARCHITECTURE
Dave King and Rod McAllister

Steel staircases in the Liverpool School of Architecture are simply detailed for ease of assembly and visual economy.

1

1 There are eight staircases in the new school; the main staircase connects the two studio levels. Stairs are fabricated in steel with plate strings. Treads are formed from angle trays bolted to the strings through shaped spacers with either rubber-covered flat plate surfaces or galvanised durbar-pattern plate on outside escape stairs.

Acknowledgment
The editors acknowledge the help of John Winter of John Winter and Associates in the preparation of this article.

In such a simple multi-level space, the staircases and handrailing are of prime importance and they use techniques and imagery in sympathy with the roof structure above.

Staircases are detailed as gangways with articulated fixings at top and bottom that clearly define the structure, means of attachment and method of adjustment to account for site tolerances. Similar flash gaps articulate the steel treads and strings which are of simple 300 × 20 mm ms flats. Securing bolts are elegantly countersunk and clearly expressed. In fact, everything about this building is clearly expressed, as it is seen as a teaching instrument, and construction and fixings are all on view. As so often happens, clarity is bought at the price of having a lot of places to clean.

The central staircase is 1500 mm wide and functions as viewing platform, meeting place and raked seating for lectures and juries.

Tubular handrailing, and the short handrail support bracket above each upright, are in stainless steel, a durable and relatively expensive material, as the architects accepted the importance of this element. Balustrade uprights are of 8 mm ms plate, press-brake folded into an 80 × 60 mm channel section. The tight radius bends pushed cold bending techniques to the limit and short tears are apparent at the top of the uprights—not structurally significant, but not elegant.

Stainless steel cables, 4 mm dia, between the uprights form the balustrade infill. These have been neatly detailed. The wires pass through lathe-turned bobbins, tapped to the rear face of the uprights, and terminate in swaged threaded ends passing through a shaped washer and tensioned with a nut. This system avoids the need for ungainly bottle screws or turn-buckles.

Misuse, such as a person standing or jumping on the cables, could eventually cause unsightly slackness, but this can easily be remedied by a maintenance man with a spanner.

Further detailed considerations include:
● staircases and balustrading were manufactured off site and assembled as a 'kit of parts'. Extensive use of slotted holes and machined packers enabled the system to be aligned and adjusted on site
● the paint finish is micaceous iron oxide primer with a silicon alkyd aluminium top coat which retains its sheen. Conventional silver paints tend to chalk quickly
● treads are covered with ribbed rubber flooring.

The studio space is designated as a 'place of assembly' under the Building Regulations which require a maximum of 16 risers per flight. The 19-riser configuration of the main stair is the result of a waiver, but is extremely pleasant to negotiate due to its generous width and easy going. ■

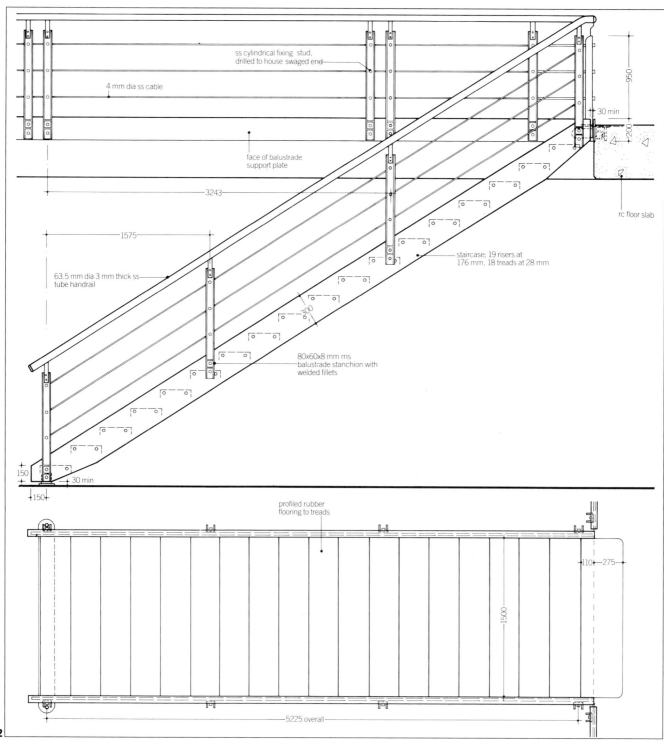

ss cylindrical fixing stud, drilled to house swaged end

4 mm dia ss cable

face of balustrade support plate

950

30 min

200

rc floor slab

3243

1575

staircase; 19 risers at 176 mm, 18 treads at 28 mm

63.5 mm dia 3 mm thick ss tube handrail

300

80x60x8 mm ms balustrade stanchion with welded fillets

150

30 min

150

profiled rubber flooring to treads

110 275

1500

5225 overall

2

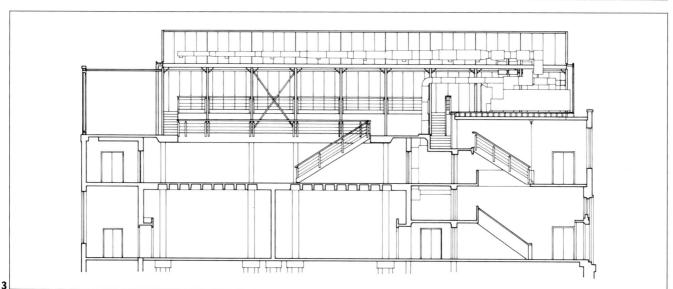

3

4

5

2 Plan and elevation of the main stair.
3 Cross-section through the new studio.
4 The main stair is axially located beneath a triangular rooflight, and uses materials and technology similar to that of the roof structure.
5 The staircase beneath the plant room, named the 'hanging stair'. Because an existing landing was unable to offer sufficient support, the new stair is hung on tension rods from an overhead beam.
6 Isometric details on the top, typical and bottom treads of the main stair.

Credits
location Abercromby Square, Liverpool
client University of Liverpool
architects Dave King and Rod McAllister in association with the Gerald Beech Partnership
quantity surveyors John Dansken & Purdie, Gordon Lees, Alan Kennaugh
M & E services University of Liverpool, Building Services Department, Dave Durton, Henry Gun-why
structural engineers Roy Billington Associates, John Dale, Dave Harding
main contractor A. Monk Building and Civil Engineering
site agent Tim Langley
steelwork Royden Engineering
handrailing Lemming and Wren
M10 paint Leigh Paints
silicon alkyd aluminium Croda Paints
flooring Jaymart Rubber & Plastics

Photo credit
Photographs by Julie Phipps.

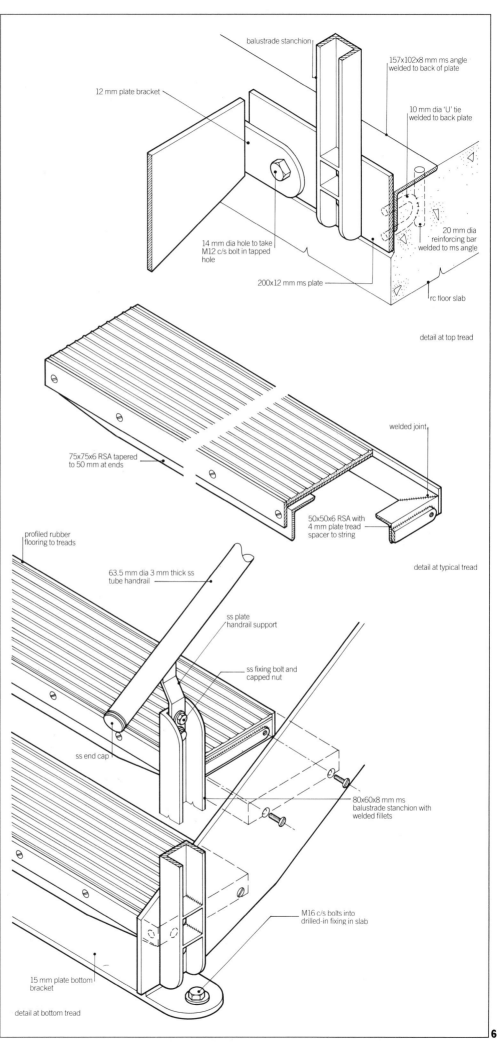

balustrade stanchion
12 mm plate bracket
157x102x8 mm ms angle welded to back of plate
10 mm dia 'U' tie welded to back plate
14 mm dia hole to take M12 c/s bolt in tapped hole
20 mm dia reinforcing bar welded to ms angle
200x12 mm ms plate
rc floor slab

detail at top tread

75x75x6 RSA tapered to 50 mm at ends
welded joint
50x50x6 RSA with 4 mm plate tread spacer to string

detail at typical tread

profiled rubber flooring to treads
63.5 mm dia 3 mm thick ss tube handrail
ss plate handrail support
ss fixing bolt and capped nut
ss end cap
80x60x8 mm ms balustrade stanchion with welded fillets
M16 c/s bolts into drilled-in fixing in slab
15 mm plate bottom bracket

detail at bottom tread

6

STEEL STAIRCASE
PRIVATE HOUSING
Richard Rogers and Partners

Steel staircases with tubular steel balustrades link the two roof-top terrace levels to each of the penthouses in the riverside housing blocks at Hammersmith.

1

1 External steel staircases serve paired penthouse flats, connecting upper and lower terrace levels. Staircases and balustrading were factory-assembled and painted. Minor scratches suffered during erection were touched up on site.

Acknowledgment
The editors acknowledge the help of John Campbell of Farrell and Company, and Lionel Friedland of Pentarch in the preparation of this article.

The roof of each housing block is shared by two penthouses. These areas are subdivided to provide terraces in addition to the standard tubular steel balconies between the blocks.

The developers required each penthouse to have its own roof access. Originally, there was to have been an internal staircase and roof-top conservatory to each penthouse. These were omitted as part of a cost-saving exercise, and replaced with the external steel staircases.

Staircase strings and quadrant landing frame are of perforated 229 x 76 mm ms channels. The treads and landing are of open square grid, galvanised ms floor grating, bolted to the strings.

At the base of the stairs, the channel strings are supported on two 48 mm diameter stainless steel spigots on plates bolted to the roof slab. The asphalt roofing is dressed up on stainless steel expanded metal mesh welded to the spigot.

A combined, weld-jointed ms locating bar and weathering cone is sleeve-fitted and bolted on to each spigot. The locating bars are bolted through plates welded to the underside of the channel strings. Oversized locating holes in these plates allow a fixing tolerance for thermal movement in the staircase steelwork without deforming the spigot which could consequently crack the asphalt dressing and allow water penetration.

The stair landing is supported on a tubular ms 'gallows' bracket bolted back to the

concrete frame. All fixing plates and bolts behind the face of the brick cladding are of stainless steel.

Further detailed considerations include:
● stainless steel spigots are bolted directly to the rc roof slab, forming a cold bridge
● asphalt is dressed up the spigot to the recommended height of 150 mm, but this should ideally be above finished paving level rather than asphalt deck level
● 8 mm pvc pads are used below terrace pavings instead of adjustable spacers. This is a cheap detail and gives a shallower roof build-up, but pavings cannot be levelled
● asphalt upstands at terrace edges are only 50-60 mm where screed thickness is greatest. Finished terrace paving level coincides with the top of the creasing tile dpc and brick coping bedding, increasing the likelihood of rain-water penetration of the dpc and frost damage due to trapped water in mortar joints
● mild steel strings and balustrading were grit-blasted and painted as follows: aluminium metal spray, two-pack etch prime, one coat zinc phosphate chlorinated rubber alkyd, chlorinated rubber undercoat, white alkyd top coat. Paint finish is specified to give five years to first maintenance, though leases specify only three years.

Staircase and terrace balustrading is of tubular steel uprights with horizontal rails that echo the nautical theme of the balconies below. ■

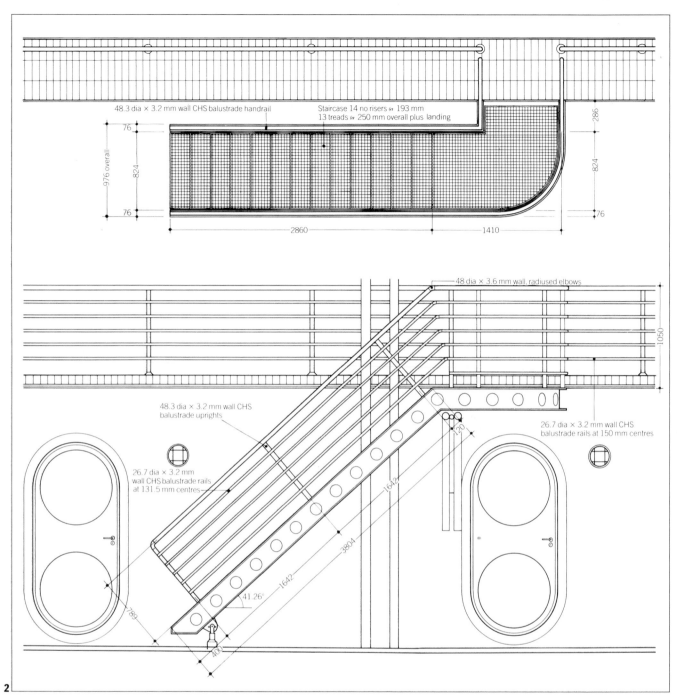

48.3 dia × 3.2 mm wall CHS balustrade handrail

Staircase 14 no risers @ 193 mm
13 treads @ 250 mm overall plus landing

76

976 overall

824

76

286

824

76

2860

1410

48 dia × 3.6 mm wall, radiused elbows

1050

48.3 dia × 3.2 mm wall CHS
balustrade uprights

26.7 dia × 3.2 mm wall CHS
balustrade rails at 150 mm centres

26.7 dia × 3.2 mm
wall CHS balustrade rails
at 131.5 mm centres

1642

3804

1642

41.26°

789

400

2

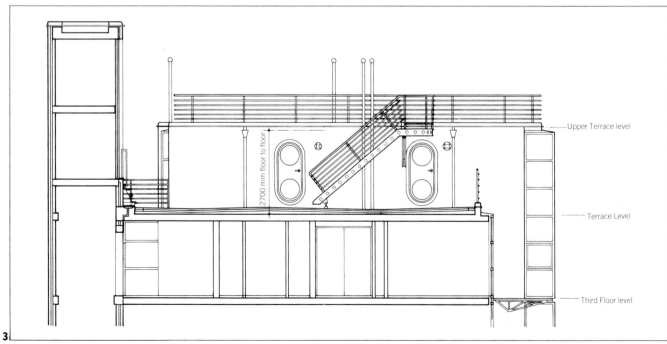

2700 mm floor to floor

Upper Terrace level

Terrace Level

Third Floor level

3

4

5

2 Elevation and plan of external staircase.
3 Section through penthouse terrace showing location of staircases.
4, 5 Details of open square grid treads and channel strings.
6 Isometric details at the landing gallows bracket, top, and supporting spigots at terrace level below. Preformed dpc cloaks above the spigot bracket brickwork junctions have been omitted for clarity.

Credits
location Rainville Road, London W6
client Croudace Construction
architect Richard Rogers and Partners: Peter Angrave (project architect), Paul Cook, Ian Gibson, Marco Goldschmied, Sarah Grenville, Ian Hopton, Tim Inskip, Janette Mackie, Mark Roche, Richard Rogers, John Young
quantity surveyor Melvyn Newell
mechanical and electrical engineers The Sinnett Partnership
structural engineer Hay Barry & Partners
landscape architects Rendel & Branch
main contractor Croudace Construction
steel staircases and balustrading Nusteel Structures

Photo credit
Photographs by Padraig Boyle.

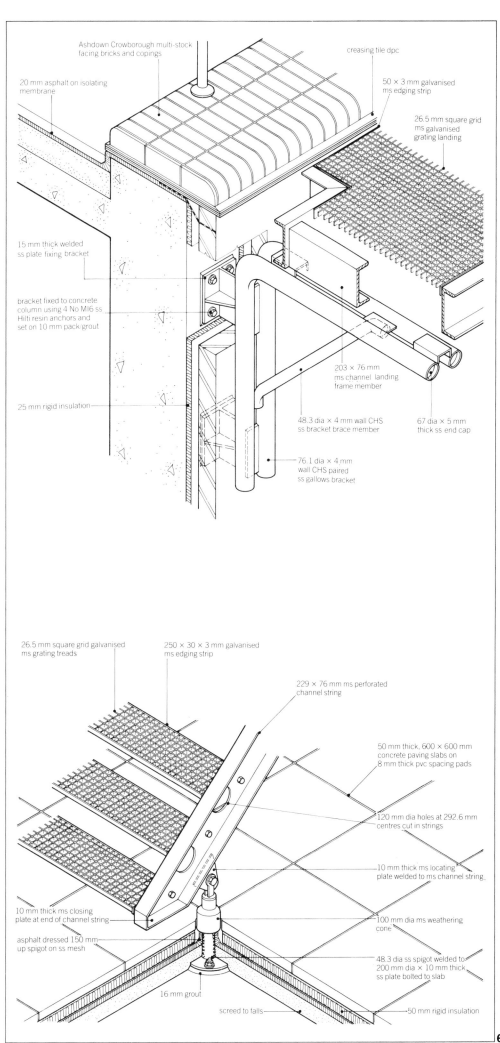

Ashdown Crowborough multi-stock facing bricks and copings

creasing tile dpc

20 mm asphalt on isolating membrane

50 × 3 mm galvanised ms edging strip

26.5 mm square grid ms galvanised grating landing

15 mm thick welded ss plate fixing bracket

bracket fixed to concrete column using 4 No M16 ss Hilti resin anchors and set on 10 mm pack/grout

25 mm rigid insulation

203 × 76 mm ms channel landing frame member

48.3 dia × 4 mm wall CHS ss bracket brace member

67 dia × 5 mm thick ss end cap

76.1 dia × 4 mm wall CHS paired ss gallows bracket

26.5 mm square grid galvanised ms grating treads

250 × 30 × 3 mm galvanised ms edging strip

229 × 76 mm ms perforated channel string

50 mm thick, 600 × 600 mm concrete paving slabs on 8 mm thick pvc spacing pads

120 mm dia holes at 292.6 mm centres cut in strings

10 mm thick ms locating plate welded to ms channel string

10 mm thick ms closing plate at end of channel string

asphalt dressed 150 mm up spigot on ss mesh

100 mm dia ms weathering cone

48.3 dia ss spigot welded to 200 mm dia × 10 mm thick ss plate bolted to slab

16 mm grout

screed to falls

50 mm rigid insulation

6

STEEL STAIRCASE
WAREHOUSE AND OFFICES
Denton Scott Associates

First-floor office areas in the Schwarzkopf headquarters building are served by a pair of independently supported steel escape staircases.

1

1 The escape staircases are located in the recessed core areas that separate the warehouse and offices. They are sheltered from the elements by the deep roof overhang.

The Schwarzkopf building has mixed usage, with two floors of offices at the front and a large double-height warehouse behind. Between the two areas is a service core containing office entrances, lavatories, an internal staircase and a pair of external escape staircases. These are located symmetrically on either side of the plan in the roofed recess between the warehouse and offices, and are sheltered by the deep overhanging eaves that protect them from exposure to rain and snow.

The staircases are fabricated from welded tubular mild steel, like the roof structure and projecting eaves supports, and detailed in a similar way, with articulated junctions and a clearly established hierarchy of component elements.

The staircases are self-supporting structures, propped below the landing by a 139.7 mm dia CHS column with bifurcated, tied struts, which are welded to the strings. The column has a 10 mm thick welded base plate bolted to a mass concrete foundation. At ground level, the CHS strings bear on welded 8 mm thick base plates anchored to the concrete plinth foundation.

Further detailed considerations include:
● the strings are of 114.3 mm dia × 6.3 mm wall CHS lengths cranked horizontally at the top and bottom with welded closing plates at each end
● treads and landing are of 4.5 mm thick galvanised chequer plate with folded-down nosings, bolted on to 5 mm thick ms plate supports welded to the strings. There is a 20 mm flash gap between the landing and the walls at first-floor level to emphasise the staircase's structural independence
● balustrading is minimal: a 48.3 mm dia × 3.2 mm wall CHS handrail is supported by 60.3 mm dia × 5 mm wall CHS uprights at 1540 mm centres. The uprights are spaced off the strings by short lengths of 48.3 mm dia tube. The mid-rail is of 33.7 mm dia × 3.2 mm wall CHS tube. All cut tube ends have welded ms closing plates
● tubular mild steel components are not galvanised. Paintwork was factory-applied and the specification is intended to give maximum protection in exposed conditions. Steelwork was blast-cleaned followed by one coat two-pack phosphate epoxy primer, one coat high-build epoxy micaceous iron oxide, finished with two coats luxol silicone alkyd enamel, coloured dark grey.

Lateral bracing is provided by two chemically fixed anchor connections through the CHS strings into the adjacent blockwork wall at landing level. To facilitate this, access holes were predrilled in the strings. The anchoring bolts and bolt-hole are concealed by 48.3 mm dia tubular spacing sleeves welded to the string. The access holes were made good, welds ground off and paintwork touched up after fixing on site. ■

Acknowledgment
The editors acknowledge the help of John Campbell of Terry Farrell and Company and Lionel Friedland of Pentarch in the preparation of this article.

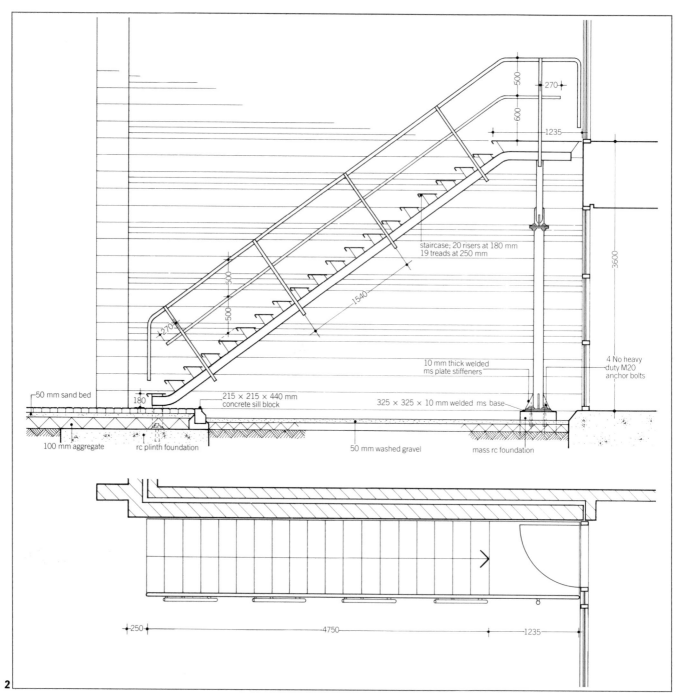

staircase; 20 risers at 180 mm
19 treads at 250 mm

270

500

600

1235

500

500

270

1540

3600

10 mm thick welded
ms plate stiffeners

4 No heavy
duty M20
anchor bolts

50 mm sand bed

180

215 × 215 × 440 mm
concrete sill block

325 × 325 × 10 mm welded ms base

100 mm aggregate

rc plinth foundation

50 mm washed gravel

mass rc foundation

250

4750

1235

2

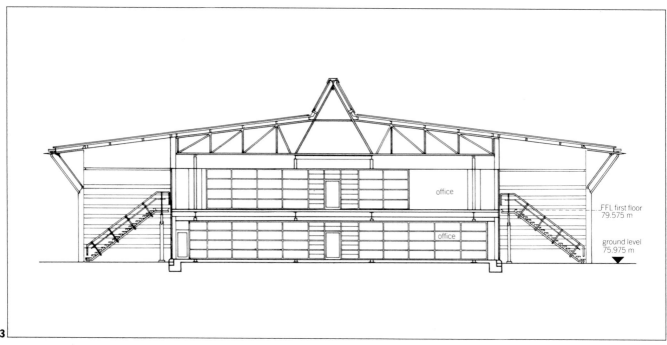

office

office

FFL first floor
79.575 m

ground level
75.975 m

3

4

2 Plan and elevation of the escape staircase.
3 Cross-section through office area showing location of escape staircases.
4 Detail at ground level. The CHS strings bear on welded 8 mm thick base plates anchored to the concrete plinth foundations. The plates are mostly concealed by the paving blocks that are used throughout the open recessed core areas, so that the ends of the strings appear to float clear of the ground.
5 Isometric details. Top, the support structure at the landing, showing lateral bracing connections to the blockwork wall. Bottom, the detail at ground level, cut away to show plate fixings to the concrete plinth foundation.

Credits
location Penn Road, Aylesbury, Bucks
client Schwarzkopf
architect Denton Scott Associates
design director Andrew Scott
project architect Robert de Grey
assistant architects Adrian Morrow, Chris Bannister
quantity surveyor Davis Langdon and Everest
structure and services Buro Happold
main contractor Western Counties Construction
subcontractor, main and escape stairs L. G. Kimber (Engineering)

Photo credit
Photographs by Peter Cook.

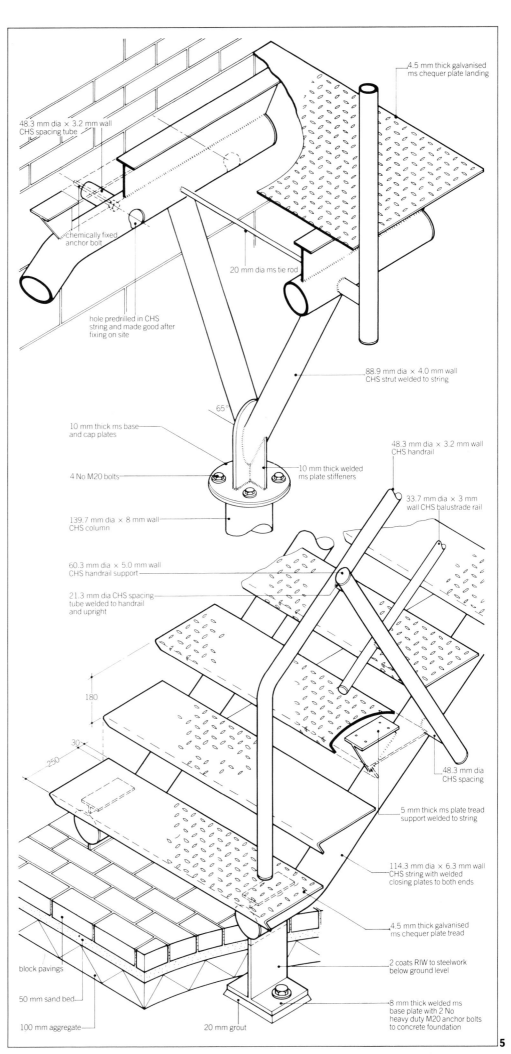

48.3 mm dia × 3.2 mm wall CHS spacing tube

chemically fixed anchor bolt

hole predrilled in CHS string and made good after fixing on site

10 mm thick ms base and cap plates

4 No M20 bolts

139.7 mm dia × 8 mm wall CHS column

60.3 mm dia × 5.0 mm wall CHS handrail support

21.3 mm dia CHS spacing tube welded to handrail and upright

65°

250

30

180

block pavings

50 mm sand bed

100 mm aggregate

20 mm grout

4.5 mm thick galvanised ms chequer plate landing

20 mm dia ms tie rod

88.9 mm dia × 4.0 mm wall CHS strut welded to string

48.3 mm dia × 3.2 mm wall CHS handrail

33.7 mm dia × 3 mm wall CHS balustrade rail

10 mm thick welded ms plate stiffeners

48.3 mm dia CHS spacing

5 mm thick ms plate tread support welded to string

114.3 mm dia × 6.3 mm wall CHS string with welded closing plates to both ends

4.5 mm thick galvanised ms chequer plate tread

2 coats RIW to steelwork below ground level

8 mm thick welded ms base plate with 2 No heavy duty M20 anchor bolts to concrete foundation

5

STEEL STAIRCASE
ARTIST'S STUDIO
Eric Parry Associates

This staircase in the studio for the artist Tom Phillips has painted steel plate treads and strings and minimalist square-section balustrading.

1

1 From the first-floor reading area in Tom Phillips' studio, a steel stair leads to the mezzanine level, intended as a drawing and portraiture studio.

Acknowledgment
The editors acknowledge the help of David Turnbull of Stirling Wilford and Associates in the preparation of this article.

The studios of sculptor Antony Gormley and painter Tom Phillips are grouped around an existing courtyard behind a terrace of shops in Camberwell, south-east London.

Tom Phillips' studio is established as a tower inserted into an existing wall, providing a densely planned, vertically organised sequence of spaces. The tower is elaborately considered and detailed. Within the tower the main stair to the first floor wraps around a column. The column is finished in a yew veneer and contains a series of niches and shelves. From the first-floor reading area a steel stair rises to a mezzanine level intended for drawing or portraiture. The steel stair can be thought of as the 'blossoming' or unfolding outward of the interior of the tower toward the roof.

The working drawings for the stair were quite rudimentary. Considerable responsibility was placed on the steelwork fabricators. The combination of a straight flight and a spiral flight with the architect's idea of 'blossoming' suggested an extremely complex profile for the internal string.

Both treads and stringers are cut from flat ms plate terminating at mezzanine level on a 76 × 152 mm ms channel edge profile installed by others. Clearly, profile drawings and typical details cannot provide sufficient information to describe precisely the curve of the internal stringer. No setting-out dimensions were given.

The start and finish locations were marked on site and the fabricators took their own dimensions to make up the stair. It was agreed that the spiral section of stair would be fabricated around an ms circular hollow section of 8 mm wall thickness, which would then be flame-cut to the architect's site-marked curve after fabrication was completed in principle. To avoid distortion of the tube, a hit-and-miss method was used, ie cutting in discontinuous short runs and allowing a period for the metal to cool between cuts.

The treads are constructed from 6 mm ms plate welded on to a 25 × 25 ms angle. Welding has been controlled impressively with the length of weld and centres between them identical for each tread.

Balustrade framing is minimal and constructed from small-section mild steel flat section. The top rail is identified as the most important by being separated visually from the rectangular profile paired verticals by a cranked 12 mm diameter mild steel rod. The paired verticals provide the dominant connection between the flank of the straight flight of the steel stair and the main stair below, and support a toughened glass plate. The glass allows visual continuity between the two stairs but prevents the risk of a fall.

The stair is finished with four coats of red oxide primer. This treatment was requested by the client after the stair was installed. ■

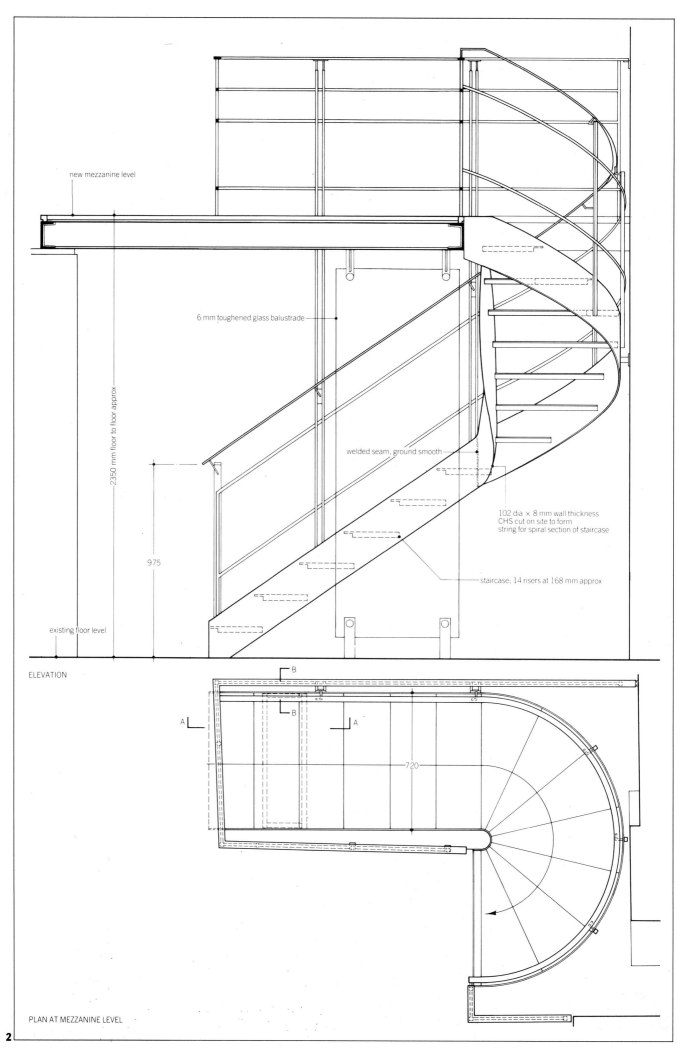

new mezzanine level

6 mm toughened glass balustrade

2350 mm floor to floor approx

975

existing floor level

welded seam, ground smooth

102 dia × 8 mm wall thickness
CHS cut on site to form
string for spiral section of staircase

staircase; 14 risers at 168 mm approx

ELEVATION

B

B

A

A

720

PLAN AT MEZZANINE LEVEL

3

2 Elevation and plan of the staircase.
3 The balustrading is of welded square and flat-section mild steel finished with red oxide primer at the client's request.
4 Part-section through the stair treads in the lower, straight flight, and section at a larger scale through string and handrail.

Credits
location Camberwell, London SE15
client Tom Phillips and Antony Gormley
architect Eric Parry Associates
partner in charge/project architect Eric Parry and Nello Gregori
assistant architect William Mann
contract manager Eric Parry Associates
site supervision Eric Parry, Nello Gregori, David Dernie, William Mann
structural engineer Michael J. Pereira
subcontractors: structural steelwork Robo Engineering, *specialist metalwork* Lee Warren.

Photo credit
Photographs by Martin Charles

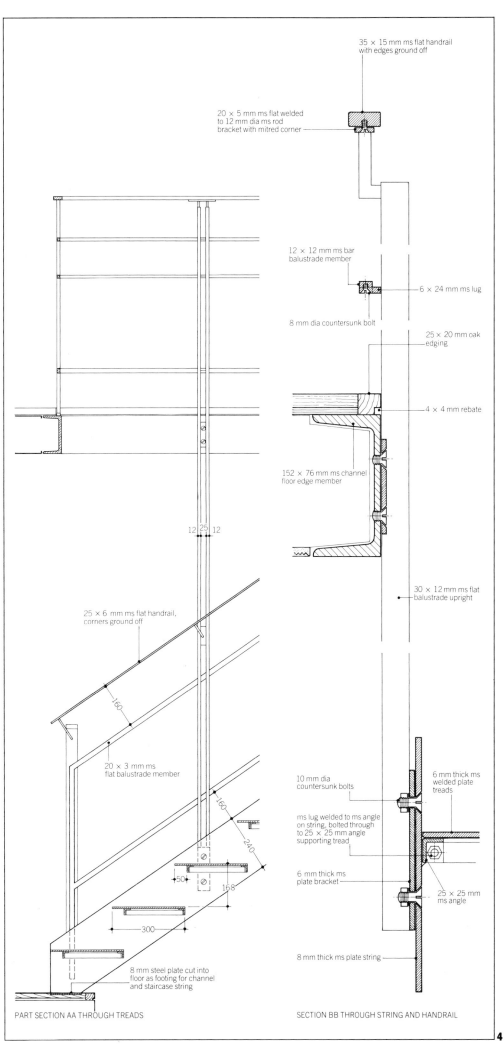

35 × 15 mm ms flat handrail with edges ground off

20 × 5 mm ms flat welded to 12 mm dia ms rod bracket with mitred corner

12 × 12 mm ms bar balustrade member

6 × 24 mm ms lug

8 mm dia countersunk bolt

25 × 20 mm oak edging

4 × 4 mm rebate

152 × 76 mm ms channel floor edge member

30 × 12 mm ms flat balustrade upright

25 × 6 mm ms flat handrail, corners ground off

12 25 12

20 × 3 mm ms flat balustrade member

160

160

240

50

168

300

10 mm dia countersunk bolts

6 mm thick ms welded plate treads

ms lug welded to ms angle on string, bolted through to 25 × 25 mm angle supporting tread

6 mm thick ms plate bracket

25 × 25 mm ms angle

8 mm thick ms plate string

8 mm steel plate cut into floor as footing for channel and staircase string

PART SECTION AA THROUGH TREADS

SECTION BB THROUGH STRING AND HANDRAIL

4

COURTROOM AND FITTINGS
LAW COURTS
Evans and Shalev

The Truro Courts of Justice building has three courtrooms of varying size. Each is air-conditioned and has purpose designed fixed furniture.

1

1 Courtroom number one is the largest of the three. It is daylit from skylights along two sides.

The three courts are composed of similar elements and have a strong gridded theme applied to ceilings, walls and purpose designed benches. This theme has minor variations which, with changes in size and lighting, give each court a distinctive character.

The courts are fully air-conditioned and day-lit by means of perimeter skylighting, with a large high-level window in the dual-purpose court. Services are arranged so that ceilings need not be demountable in order to gain access to voids. Supply air diffusers are fully integrated with the ceiling pattern. Extract apertures are situated in the vertical faces of the dropped ceiling assembly and are generally invisible. Supplementary artificial lighting is by means of uplighters.

Avoiding the problem of access allowed the ceilings to be purpose designed rather than relying on a patent system. Ceilings are made from flat panels of 25 mm fire-resistant board with applied moulded softwood sections painted white, which, unless a close inspection is made, easily passes for fibrous plaster.

Panels are fixed on a 1200 x 1200 mm grid back to 100 x 50 mm treated softwood framing with acoustic insulation quilt above. Duct inspection routes are floored with softwood T&G boarding.

Purpose-made benches are of ash veneer on MDF with solid ash mouldings and nosings. The ash is stained grey. Benches are supported on mild steel subframes.

The side and rear courtroom walls are panelled to a dado above the door heads and then finished full height with spray-applied acoustic plaster. Curved walls behind judges' benches are panelled in profiled softwood vertical T&G boarding. All woodwork is oil-painted white.

Further detailed considerations include:
● the method of ceiling construction requires considerable skill to ensure that all mitres are cut accurately and finished flush on the face
● movement or shrinkage in the width of softwood mouldings and T&G panelling could cause paint finishes to crack and spoil the appearance
● unframed glass security screens attached to some benches are made from laminated glass. Edges of this type of glass are unsightly and, depending upon security requirements, toughened glass is an easily edge polished and bevelled alternative
● spray-applied acoustic plaster is an imprecise material prone to surface patterning or patching. Acoustic plastered surfaces are mostly skylit, which highlights these irregularities.

In contrast to the white walls and ceilings and pale grey benches, the carpeting and seating upholstery is of a deep royal blue. In combination with the colour scheme, natural lighting helps to 'humanise' the courtrooms and create a calming atmosphere for areas that are often centres for nervous tension. ■

Acknowledgement
The editors acknowledge the help of Roland Gibbard of YRM Interiors in the preparation of this article.

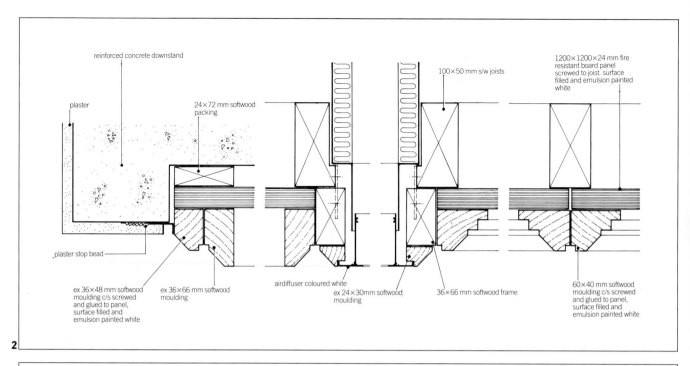

reinforced concrete downstand

plaster

24×72 mm softwood packing

100×50 mm s/w joists

1200×1200×24 mm fire resistant board panel screwed to joist. surface filled and emulsion painted white

plaster stop bead

ex 36×48 mm softwood moulding c/s screwed and glued to panel, surface filled and emulsion painted white

ex 36×66 mm softwood moulding

airdiffuser coloured white

ex 24×30mm softwood moulding

36×66 mm softwood frame

60×40 mm softwood moulding c/s screwed and glued to panel, surface filled and emulsion painted white

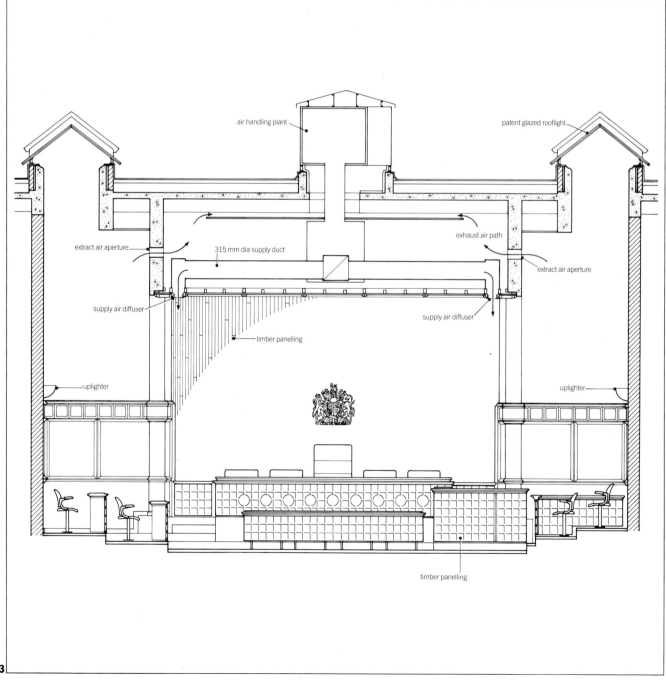

air handling plant

patent glazed rooflight

extract air aperture

315 mm dia supply duct

exhaust air path

extract air aperture

supply air diffuser

supply air diffuser

timber panelling

uplighter

uplighter

timber panelling

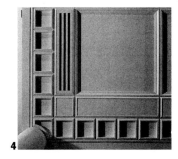

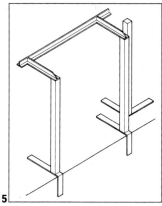

2 Ceiling panelling details.
3 Section through courtroom number one.
4 Air supply diffusers are fully integrated into the ceiling pattern.
5, 6 Isometric details of jury bench. Benches are of ash veneer on MDF with solid ash mouldings and supported on a mild steel subframe. The frame locates on spigots welded to plates that are countersunk bolted to the floor screed.

Credits
location Edward Street, Truro
architects Evans and Shalev; Eldred Evans, David Shalev, Charles Mador
quantity surveyor MDA; Richard Pope, Kevin Heaton
structural engineer Anthony Hunt Associates; Stephen Morley, Alan Smith
services engineer Max Fordham and partners, Max Fordham, David Lindsay
contractor Dudley Coles
contract manager Bryan Hammond
site agent Tony Luke
clerk of works Wilf Ballm
project managers Property Services Agency, Martin Brooks, John Whiting, Jim Dunaway, Len Froom-Lewis
m & e subcontractors: mechanical installation Haden Young, Bristol *duct work* Contract Air, *electrical installation* Staveley Industries, *environmental controls* Satchwell Control System, *communication and fire alarms* Static Systems, *courtroom fittings* Dudley Coles Shopfitters, *crests and signs* Roman Halter, *floor screeds and tiling* J.H. Lidstone, *acoustic plaster* Morceau Fire Protection, *floor coverings* Ritelay Floors, *internal doors* H.C. Bridgman (Joinery), *louvred grilles* Waterloo Ozonair, *ceilings* Gary Richardson Ceilings.

Photo credit
Photographs by Martin Charles

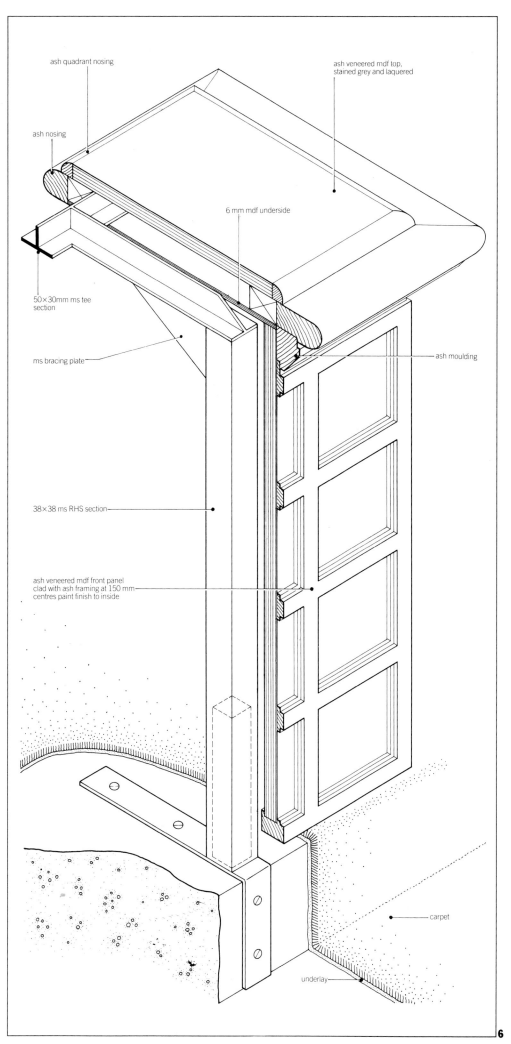

ash quadrant nosing

ash veneered mdf top, stained grey and laquered

ash nosing

6 mm mdf underside

50×30mm ms tee section

ash moulding

ms bracing plate

38×38 ms RHS section

ash veneered mdf front panel clad with ash framing at 150 mm centres paint finish to inside

carpet

underlay

6

VANITORY UNIT
RECORDING EQUIPMENT FACTORY
Michael Hopkins and Partners

Freestanding vanitory units in the washrooms at the Solid State Logic factory were purpose-designed to avoid cantilevering basins from the partition walls.

1 Vanitory units in male and female washrooms are identically detailed. Soap dispensers or soap dishes have not been provided—which leads to bars of soap being left randomly on the work-top—a minor but irritating omission.

Acknowledgment
The editors acknowledge the help of Roland Gibbard of YRM Interiors in the preparation of this article.

Washrooms and lavatories are located on the ground floor and constructed using a steel-faced Hauserman partition system which is used in glazed form as cellular office walling elsewhere in the building.

Generally when fitting out washrooms, either basins or vanitory units may be installed. Each option has its advantages and drawbacks. Basins are normally cantilevered, leaving an uninterrupted floor surface for easy cleaning, but also require associated shelf space for placing articles when washing—a detail that is often omitted. The vanitory unit provides a horizontal surface but this requires regular cleaning to ensure that the top is kept dry and free from dirt so that it can be used for its intended purpose.

In this case, cantilevering basins from the partitioning system would not have been practicable. The solution is a freestanding unit that avoids contact with the partition. The top is of 30 mm Sardinian grey granite—fabricated in two halves and dry-dowel-jointed for ease of handling—with standard vitreous china circular basins mounted below.

The subframe is of 108 mm diameter CHS welded steel, epoxy-powder-coated dark grey. Subframe uprights are at 1200 mm centres. Welded plates at the feet are bolted to the precast floor beams and concealed by the floor screed and finish.

The granite top is supported on screw-adjustable pads on 10 m thick profiled ms brackets welded to the subframe at 450 mm centres.

A 285 mm × 73 mm × 2700 mm long Zehnder radiavector is hung on steel brackets welded to the back of the CHS uprights. The radiators and chromed waste pipes are partially concealed by a 400 mm deep granite fascia panel, which is fixed by epoxy-grouted bolts to its own steel subframe of welded 50 × 10 mm ms flat sections epoxy-powder-coated dark grey that locates on hooks welded to the CHS uprights. Water supply pipes are clipped behind the horizontal subframe transom member and are not visible.

Further detailed considerations include:
● granite is a well proven material in this situation. A suitable alternative could be Corian. Using this material the work-top and basins can be moulded in one piece, thus avoiding the junction between top and bowl.
● The cut-out in the granite top has to be slightly smaller than the basin to allow for slight variations in basin size. Even with a good mastic joint, scum can collect at this junction if not properly cleaned.
● The top surface, size permitting, should be in one piece to reduce the number of butted grouted joints, which are especially noticeable with light-coloured granites or marbles.

Overall the vanitory unit, including the frameless circular mirrors which relate to the basin shape, is a well considered and economic solution to the problem. ■

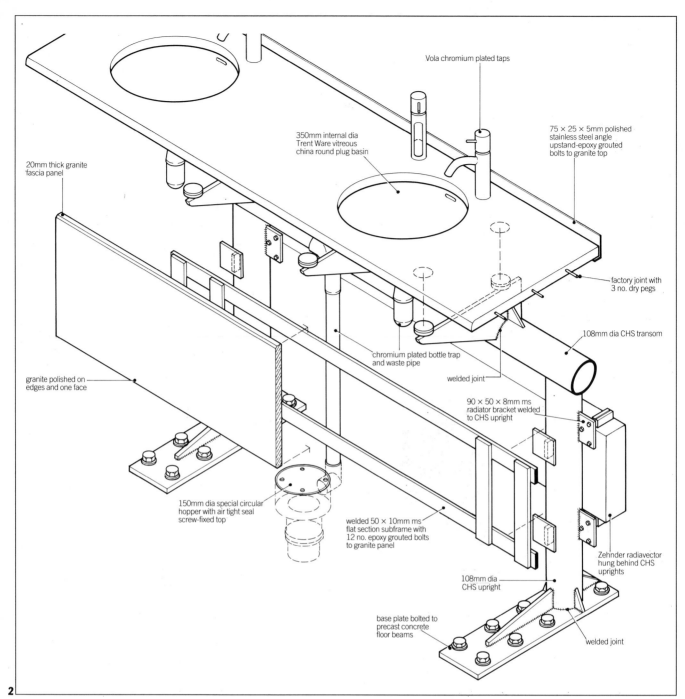

Vola chromium plated taps

350mm internal dia
Trent Ware vitreous
china round plug basin

20mm thick granite
fascia panel

75 × 25 × 5mm polished
stainless steel angle
upstand-epoxy grouted
bolts to granite top

granite polished on
edges and one face

factory joint with
3 no. dry pegs

108mm dia CHS transom

chromium plated bottle trap
and waste pipe

welded joint

90 × 50 × 8mm ms
radiator bracket welded
to CHS upright

150mm dia special circular
hopper with air tight seal
screw-fixed top

welded 50 × 10mm ms
flat section subframe with
12 no. epoxy grouted bolts
to granite panel

Zehnder radiavector
hung behind CHS
uprights

108mm dia
CHS upright

base plate bolted to
precast concrete
floor beams

welded joint

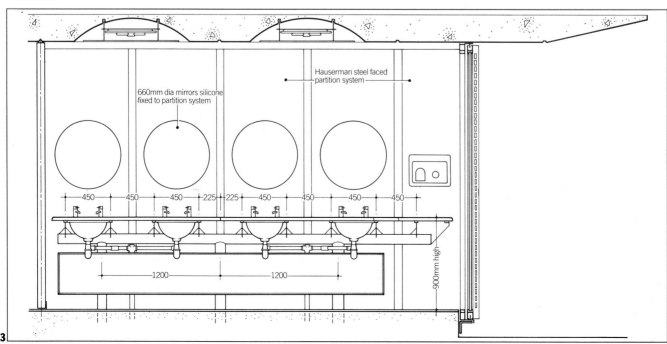

660mm dia mirrors silicone
fixed to partition system

Hauserman steel faced
partition system

450 450 450 225 225 450 450 450 450

1200   1200

900mm high

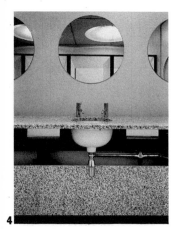

2 Cut-away isometric of vanitory unit showing subframe assembly. The stainless steel angle at the back of the work-top is intended to prevent objects falling down the gap between the work-top and wall, but has still to be fitted by the subcontractor.
3 Section through washroom.
4 Circular mirrors relate to each basin position.
5 Section through vanitory unit.

Credits
location Springhill Road, Begbroke, Oxon
client Solid State Logic
architect Michael Hopkins and Partners
partners in charge Michael Hopkins, Ian Sharratt
project architect Peter Romaniuk
assistant architects Peter Cartwright, Bill Dunster, Graham Saunders
quantity surveyor Davis Langdon and Everest, Alec Waller, Clive Lewis
structural and services engineers Buro Happold, M. Dickson, Michael Green, Peter Moseley
main contractor Walter Lawrence Project Management
project manager Peter Richardson
mechanical/plumbing Alden Heating
electrical services Drake and Skull Engineering
partitions Clestra
raised floors Floorplan Electrical
ceilings Diespecker
joinery Angoods/Spectrum
Norament rubber floor Carl Freudenberg
taps Vola
radiators Zehnder
basins Trent Ware

Photo credit
Photography by Martin Charles

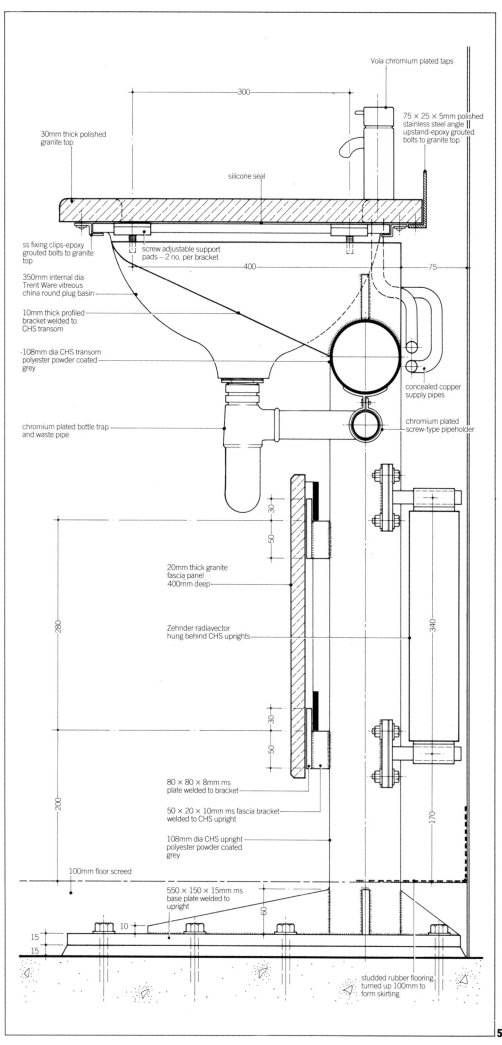

Vola chromium plated taps

75 × 25 × 5mm polished stainless steel angle upstand-epoxy grouted bolts to granite top

30mm thick polished granite top

silicone seal

ss fixing clips-epoxy grouted bolts to granite top

screw adjustable support pads – 2 no. per bracket

350mm internal dia Trent Ware vitreous china round plug basin

10mm thick profiled bracket welded to CHS transom

108mm dia CHS transom polyester powder coated grey

concealed copper supply pipes

chromium plated screw-type pipeholder

chromium plated bottle trap and waste pipe

20mm thick granite fascia panel 400mm deep

Zehnder radiavector hung behind CHS uprights

80 × 80 × 8mm ms plate welded to bracket

50 × 20 × 10mm ms fascia bracket welded to CHS upright

108mm dia CHS upright polyester powder coated grey

100mm floor screed

550 × 150 × 15mm ms base plate welded to upright

studded rubber flooring turned up 100mm to form skirting

DOORS AND SCREENS
OFFICES
Eric Parry Associates

Perimeter offices in Stanhope Properties' headquarters have fully glazed screens. The conference room has a wall of obscured glass blocks and doors faced with stainless steel.

1

1 Perimeter offices have glazed screens, with full-height (2.7 m) solid-core doors veneered with American burr walnut. Opaque panels between the doors are of white-painted 6 mm MDF to conceal the ends of partitions between offices. Experiments with translucent white glazing panels at seated eye-level have been made in some areas to increase privacy for office occupants.

Acknowledgment
The editors acknowledge the help of Roland Gibbard of YRM Interiors in the preparation of this article.

Stanhope Properties occupies offices on the fifth floor of a speculative block in the West End of London. The building has a deep plan, with a central atrium and multiple service cores, and was fitted out to a lavish but unwanted standard by the developers: suspended environmental ceilings, carpeted raised floors, mechanical and electrical services and core finishes were complete, ready for a tenant who might want 21 000 sq ft of open-plan office space.

But Stanhope Properties' requirements were more complex. It needed cellular offices for directors, executives and project managers with associated secretarial accommodation; meeting-rooms; and reception and waiting areas. On top of this, the fit-out had to take no more than 15 weeks from initial design to hand-over.

Inevitably, much of the original fabric has been retained and cellular offices are planned to make best use of the air supply outlets and light-fittings in the existing ceiling. Partitions between offices are lightweight dry-lined metal studwork built off the raised floor.

Screens between perimeter offices and inboard secretarial spaces are fully glazed to allow daylight into the plan, to maintain visual contact between cellular and shared accommodation, and to give those in deep-plan areas views of the outside world.

Screens have aluminium subframes with tapered glazing beads of polished Santos

rosewood; one side factory-fixed using a two-pack epoxy adhesive, the other fixed on site after glazing, with a mastic adhesive which allows the beads to be prized off to replace the 6 mm toughened glass.

Ends of partitions between offices are concealed by solid panels of white-painted 6 mm MDF, fitted like the glass.

The glass-block conference-room wall is one of the few 'heavy' items, and is supported by a steel channel section frame, bolted at top and bottom to the concrete floor slabs.

The 195 × 195 × 75 mm solid glass blocks are sand-blasted on one side to ensure privacy. The tolerance in each block is ± 2 mm due to the nature of the casting process. This tolerance was taken up progressively by preassembling units of six blocks, complete with acetate spacers and clear silicone joints, then building these units together on site. Final adjustments to the top frame member were made after the blocks were laid.

Glass blocks are traditionally laid with mortar bed joints. Silicone jointing is a relatively new method that gives a more discreet joint.

Conference-room doors have 44 mm thick solid cores faced with polished stainless steel. Frames are hardwood, faced in drawn stainless steel, set in a substantial subframe of welded ms channel sections. This has a grey gloss paint finish that tends to dematerialise its bulk so that the doors appear freestanding. ∎

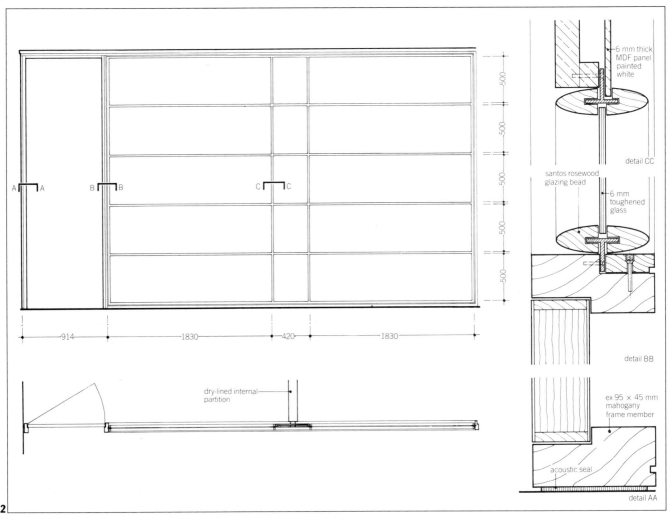

500
500
500
500
500

A | A   B | B   C | C

detail CC

6 mm thick
MDF panel
painted
white

santos rosewood
glazing bead

6 mm
toughened
glass

detail BB

ex 95 × 45 mm
mahogany
frame member

acoustic seal

detail AA

dry-lined internal
partition

914   1830   420   1830

2

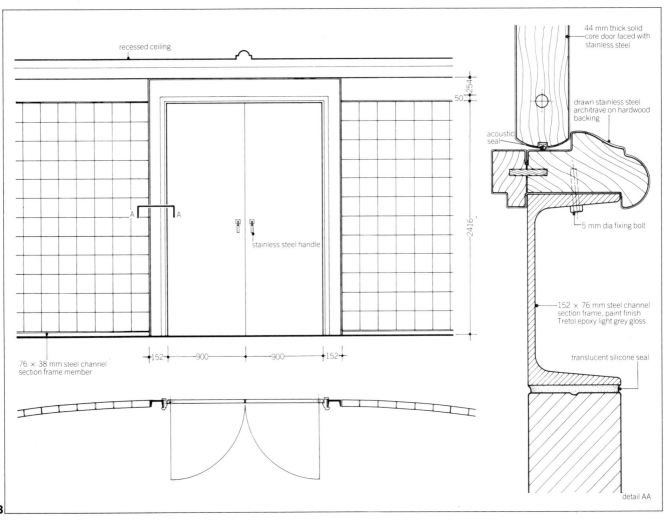

recessed ceiling

44 mm thick solid
core door faced with
stainless steel

drawn stainless steel
architrave on hardwood
backing

acoustic
seal

5 mm dia fixing bolt

A | A

stainless steel handle

76 × 38 mm steel channel
section frame member

152×900×900×152

254
50

2416

152 × 76 mm steel channel
section frame, paint finish
Tretol epoxy light grey gloss

translucent silicone seal

detail AA

3

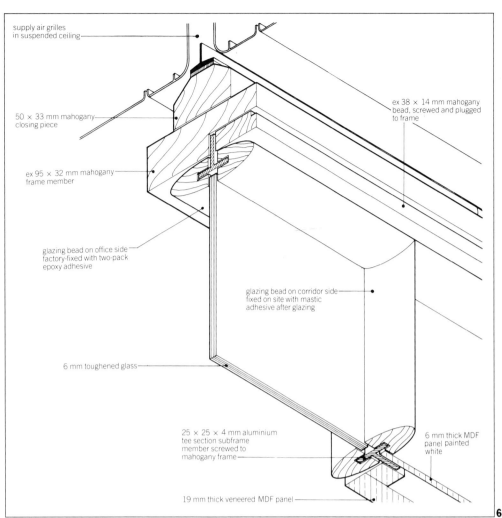

supply air grilles
in suspended ceiling

50 × 33 mm mahogany
closing piece

ex 95 × 32 mm mahogany
frame member

ex 38 × 14 mm mahogany
bead, screwed and plugged
to frame

glazing bead on office side
factory-fixed with two-pack
epoxy adhesive

glazing bead on corridor side
fixed on site with mastic
adhesive after glazing

6 mm toughened glass

25 × 25 × 4 mm aluminium
tee section subframe
member screwed to
mahogany frame

6 mm thick MDF
panel painted
white

19 mm thick veneered MDF panel

6

2 Plan, elevation and details of a
typical perimeter office glazed
screen; see 1.
3, 4, 5 Plan, elevation and details
of doors in the glass-block
conference-room wall.
6 Isometric detail at the head of a
typical glazed screen.
7 Isometric detail of
conference-room door frame.

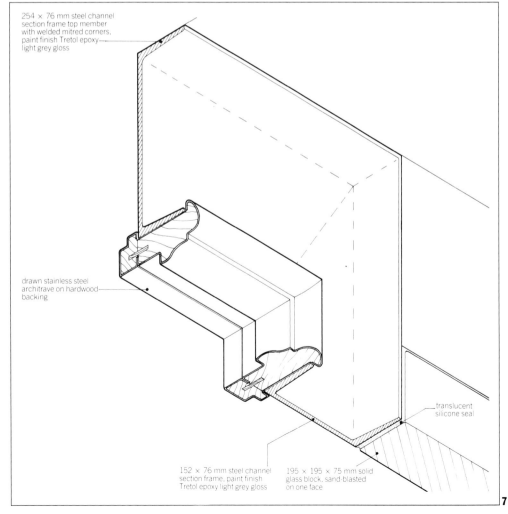

254 × 76 mm steel channel
section frame top member
with welded mitred corners,
paint finish Tretol epoxy
light grey gloss

drawn stainless steel
architrave on hardwood
backing

translucent
silicone seal

152 × 76 mm steel channel
section frame, paint finish
Tretol epoxy light grey gloss

195 × 195 × 75 mm solid
glass block, sand-blasted
on one face

7

Credits
location Fifth Floor, Lansdowne
House, Berkeley Square, London W1
client Stanhope Properties plc
architect Eric Parry Associates
structural engineer Ove Arup &
Partners
construction managers Schal
International Limited
furniture consultant Business
Design Group
mechanical and electrical services
How Engineering Services
veneered doors F. R. Shadbolt & Sons
joinery Colin Cheeseman Joinery
partitions W. A. Browne
decoration F. T. D. Decorations
drawn metal frames Drawn Metal
steelwork Donkin Construction
ironmongery Yannedis & Co
glass blocks Pittsburg Corning Corp
paints and sealants Tretol Tremco

Photo credit
Photographs by Martin Charles.

READING-ROOM LIGHTING
UNIVERSITY LIBRARY
Colin St John Wilson & Partners

The lighting system designed for the library at Queen Mary College represents a major departure from conventional practice. This elegant solution is economical, flexible and easy to maintain.

1

1 Reflectors and lighting installation seen from reading area on first floor. A typical reader's task light can be seen on the left. The uplighters are located at 2.7 m centres and project light on to the slab soffit. The latter is painted white between the external wall and the first of the exposed air ducts (which can be seen with its holed top-hat plenum above the reflectors beyond the column). Note that fluorescent tubes are only fitted to those reflectors in the book stack zone.

Acknowledgment
The editors acknowledge the help of Roland Gibbard of YRM Interiors in the preparation of this article.

The clear objective when considering overhead lighting in open-access reading-rooms is to provide adequate illumination for the readers and, within the book stacks, for selection and replacement of books. Many libraries have been designed with strip fluorescent fittings running at right angles to the stacks—the theory being that the spacing can be arranged and later changed to suit the librarian's requirements. For this method of installation to give satisfactory results the ceiling height has to be reasonably generous and the rows of fittings installed at close centres to give a good spread of light.

In the method illustrated here, purpose-made reflectors with exposed fluorescent tubes are joined to form a continuous run above the centre of each gangway. The reflectors are fixed to suspended metal channels running at right angles to the stacks. The reflectors can easily be slid along the channel as the stacks are rearranged. The lighting fittings do not run over the main circulation route between the book stacks. This enables stacks on either side to be positioned at different centres.

Located slightly above the stack tops, the reflectors provide a ceiling 'datum' above which ducts run. The breadth of the reflector reduces glare and eliminates the need for diffusers.

The reflectors extend as far as the longest possible stack length. Fluorescent tubes are installed only in those reflectors at present in book stack areas but can be easily fitted to the remaining reflectors should the book stacks expand. Beyond the reflector ends the perimeter volume (used by readers and for circulation) expands up to the white-painted soffit: this is lit by purpose-made halogen uplighters mounted on the ends of alternate ranges of reflectors.

The system appears to work well. The reflector profile directs light evenly over the full height of the shelving; the fittings are ideally positioned for easy tube replacement; and individual row switching and time-switches reduce running costs. Further detailed considerations include:
● had tendering procedures allowed the design of the lighting system to be co-ordinated with that of the book stacks an even better relationship between the two elements would have been possible
● fittings butted end-to-end do not always have exactly the same profile. Gaps could possibly be left between each fitting or more care taken in the fitting manufacture
● had economic considerations not precluded it, fluorescent tubes located centrally in the length of the reflector would look better.

This is a good, economical and flexible solution to the problem of reading-room lighting. Computer rooms that seldom require access often have a similar system of lighting between cabinets. ■

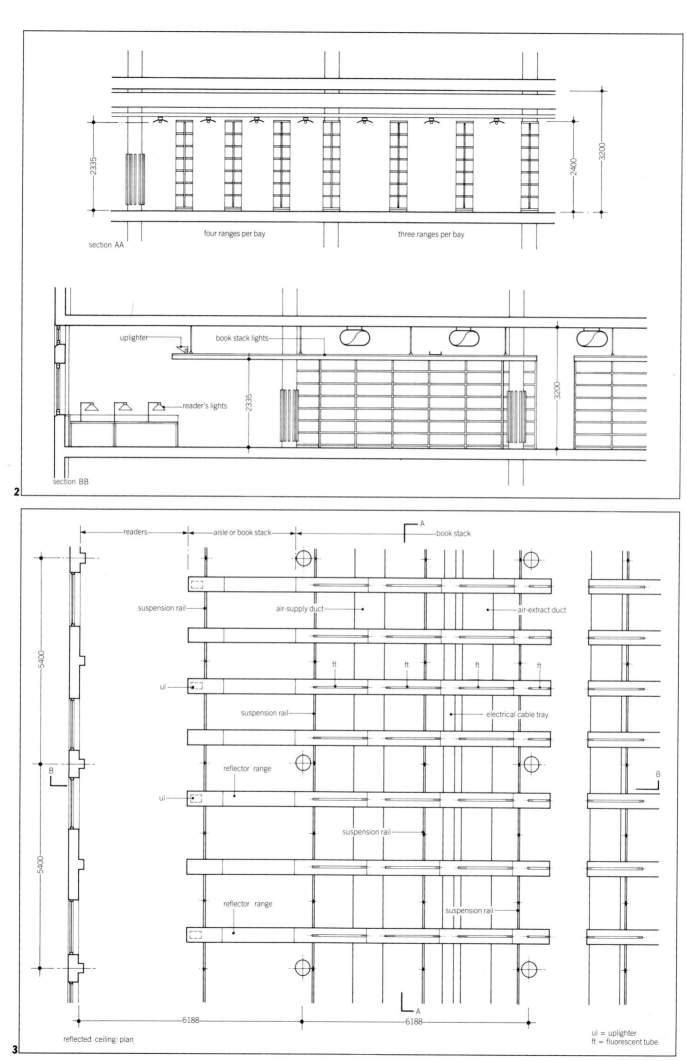

section AA

four ranges per bay

three ranges per bay

2335

2400

3200

section BB

uplighter

book stack lights

reader's lights

2335

3200

readers

aisle or book stack

book stack

A

suspension rail

air-supply duct

air-extract duct

ft   ft   ft   ft

suspension rail

electrical cable tray

ul

reflector range

B   B

ul

suspension rail

reflector range

suspension rail

5400

5400

A

6188

6188

reflected ceiling plan

ul = uplighter
ft = fluorescent tube

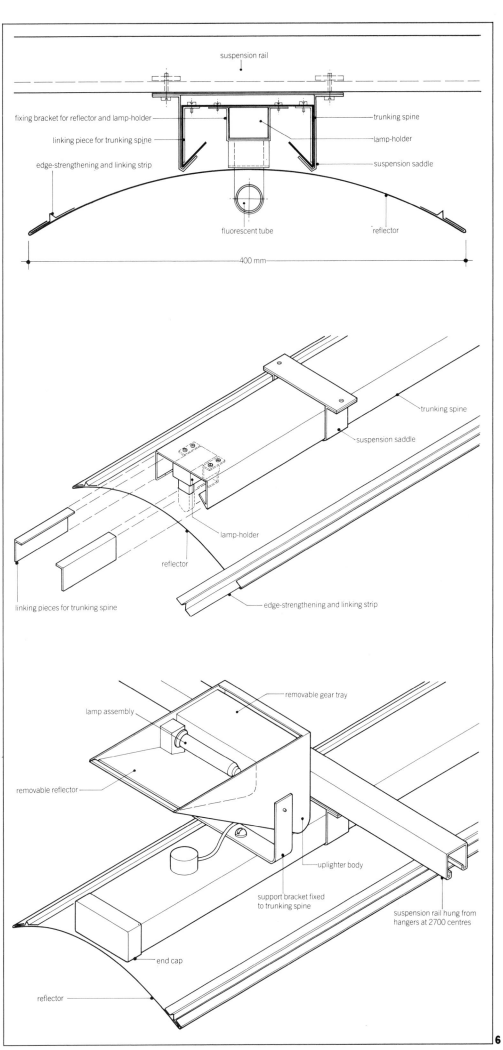

2 Sections. AA shows alternative book stack centre.
3 Reflected ceiling plan showing reflector positions related to alternative book stack centres.
4 View down typical gangway.
5 Uplighter at end of reflector range. Note the opening available for the fluorescent tube lamp-holder and the suspension rail along which the reflectors can be slid in position.
6 Reflector and lamp details. Typical cross-section (top), isometric at typical junction (centre), and isometric of end with uplighter (bottom).

Credits
location Mile End Road, London E1
client The Governing Body of Queen Mary College (University of London)
architect Colin St John Wilson & Partners
partner in charge M. J. Long
project architect Peter Brough
assistant architects Tim Hatton (sketch stage), Adolfo Spaleta
assistants Afsaneh Mirfendereski, Nick Rena
quantity surveyor Hamilton H. Turner & Son
services/electrical and mechanical engineer, structural engineer Ove Arup & Partners
main contractor Norwest Holst Construction Southern
electrical installation T. Clarke
mechanical installation R. E. Brown
special lights MID
light-support channel Unistrut (UK)
cable tray Van Geel Systems
lighting control ECS
ductwork Henry Hargreaves
air-supply terminals Trox Bros
book stacks Bruynzeel Storage Systems

Photo credit
Photographs by Martin Charles

RECEPTION DESK
CORONER'S COURT EXTENSION
Tim Ronalds Architects

This reception desk is simply formed from a series of planes, with a screen above which is similar to other screens and windows in the building.

1 View of the reception desk from the office, with the screen in its closed position.

Acknowledgment
The editors acknowledge the help of Roland Gibbard of YRM Interiors in the preparation of this article.

This single-storey extension to Walthamstow Coroner's Court is simply constructed in loadbearing masonry (brick outer leaf, 50 mm cavity with 30 mm insulation bats, 100 mm blockwork inner leaf) with an asphalted flat roof. The fairfaced brickwork (Butterley Heather Charnwood bricks with flush pointing) is also used internally in the hall, and forms the opening into which the reception desk is set.

The budget for this building was limited so the architect deliberately chose to concentrate the available resources on the joinery. The reception desk, including the screen above, is constructed in the same style as the other timberwork in the building, in American oak, stained to a dark brown (with two coats of stain and two coats of lacquer). From the office, whose plastered walls are painted white, the dark stained timber finish is particularly effective.

The dark staining of all the timber in the building (except the flooring in the hall) still allows the grain to be seen, although less readily than with a natural finish, and it can mask imperfections. It can also conceal attractively moulded joinerwork: this was not important here, however, as the building is specifically detailed so that all elements are as flush as possible—sills, copings and screens are all carefully restrained. Without obtruding into the hall space at all—in fact it is recessed rather than projecting—the reception desk

achieves its significance by its location: the screen above the desk is centrally located in the wall directly opposite the entrance.

Carefully recessing the desk on the public side has allowed the support for the screen to be simply face-fixed on the office side. The screen is hung from above, eliminating the need for dirt-collecting grooves and channels on the work surface. The door, like all the doors in the building, is an American oak-veneered solid-core flush door. The full-height and desk base panels, and the door over-panel, are all to the same specification and finish as the doors. Wherever possible, secret cleat fixings are used to allow clean junctions between planes.

The work-top is carefully positioned to line through with the window sill board on the adjacent wall.

The sliding screen, like the other screens in the building, is formed from 44 mm thick oak. The beads are mitred at the corners and checked to allow a 3 × 3 mm groove at their junctions with the stiles and transoms—to allow movement and a tolerance between the two timber members. The two parts of the transoms are screwed together and pelleted. The 4 mm obscured glass is bedded in an ordinary glazing compound.

Most elements in the reception desk are pared down to a minimum, but the way they are put together creates an elegant composition and a desk which functions well. ∎

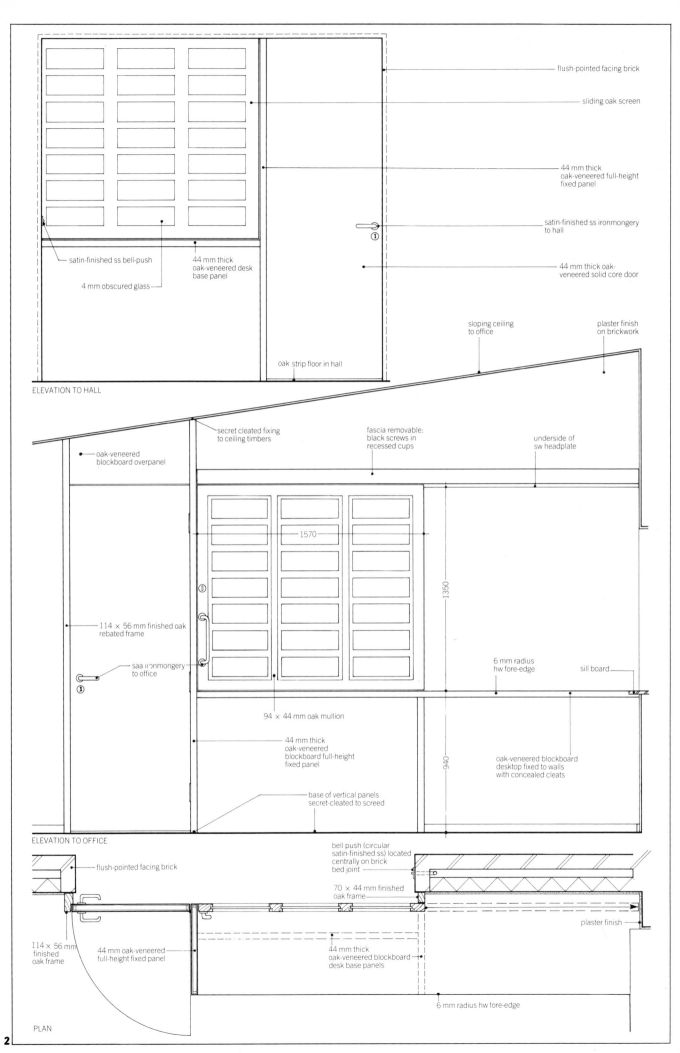

flush-pointed facing brick

sliding oak screen

44 mm thick
oak-veneered full-height
fixed panel

satin-finished ss ironmongery
to hall

44 mm thick oak-
veneered solid core door

satin-finished ss bell-push

44 mm thick
oak-veneered desk
base panel

4 mm obscured glass

oak strip floor in hall

ELEVATION TO HALL

sloping ceiling
to office

plaster finish
on brickwork

secret cleated fixing
to ceiling timbers

fascia removable:
black screws in
recessed cups

underside of
sw headplate

oak-veneered
blockboard overpanel

1570

1350

114 × 56 mm finished oak
rebated frame

saa ironmongery
to office

6 mm radius
hw fore-edge

sill board

94 × 44 mm oak mullion

44 mm thick
oak-veneered
blockboard full-height
fixed panel

940

oak-veneered blockboard
desktop fixed to walls
with concealed cleats

base of vertical panels
secret-cleated to screed

ELEVATION TO OFFICE

bell push (circular
satin-finished ss) located
centrally on brick
bed joint

flush-pointed facing brick

70 × 44 mm finished
oak frame

plaster finish

114 × 56 mm
finished
oak frame

44 mm oak-veneered
full-height fixed panel

44 mm thick
oak-veneered blockboard
desk base panels

6 mm radius hw fore-edge

PLAN

2

3

2 Elevations and plan of reception desk. The elevation to the office makes a particularly pleasing composition.
3 Close-up view from the hall of the screen, closed, at its junction with the panel forming the desktop and the full-height panel which is also one of the door jambs.
4 Isometric detail of the screen. Fixings are concealed whenever possible: the dark timber stain helps to hide fixings that have to appear on the surface, such as the pelleted screws.

15 mm plaster finish

5 mm gap

pc concrete lintel

110 × 70 mm finished sw headplate

38 × 30 mm hw batten to support track and fascia

94 × 20 mm oak fascia

94 × 44 mm oak screen head

internal transoms formed from 44 × 26 mm and 44 × 18 mm oak sections

4 mm obscured glass bedded in glazing compound colour-matched to the stained timber

94 × 44 mm oak stile

94 × 44 mm oak screen rail

groove for guide

6 mm radius hw fore-edge

44 mm thick oak-veneered blockboard desktop

44 mm thick oak-veneered desk base panel

Credits
location Queens Road, Walthamstow, London E17
client London Borough of Waltham Forest
architect Tim Ronalds Architects: Tim Ronalds, Kalliope Kontozoglou, Adam Whiteley
structural engineer Trigram Design Partnership
main contractor Richard Morris (Construction Ltd)

Photo credit
Photographs by Charlotte Wood

4

EXHIBITION DISPLAY SYSTEM
DESIGN MUSEUM
Stanton Williams

The shelving in the Design Museum's review gallery is a demountable system that can be adapted to suit changing exhibitions.

1

1 The review gallery is capable of accepting rapid change to meet the needs of various types of display by simply selecting from a range of items that have been designed, dimensioned and finished to form a unified space. Fixing positions are located at regular intervals on a standardised module to allow flexible planning.

Acknowledgment
The editors acknowledge the help of Roland Gibbard of YRM Interiors in the preparation of this article.

The Design Museum's first-floor temporary exhibition gallery is a double-height, 5.2 m high space formed by removing one floor from the existing concrete-framed warehouse.

The prime objective in fitting out this space was to provide a flexible air-conditioned facility that would allow a variety of circulation, partitioning, lighting and shelving arrangements to suit travelling exhibitions and a changing review collection. It had to be as flexible in use as a television studio but provide a 'quiet' or neutral background for the exhibits.

All services are housed within two bulkheads in the centre of the ceiling that run the full length of the gallery.

Tensioned fabric ceilings between the bulkhead and gallery walls conceal surface mounted light fittings and offer the option of strong or diffused lighting. Spotlights can be suspended below the fabric ceiling from fixing points on the gallery services module.

A Unistrut structural fixing system is used behind wall and ceiling linings. Fixing points with M24 threaded stainless steel sockets are located on a 1092 mm linear module along the gallery walls and ceiling. These fixings are strong enough to take heavy exhibits—a motor bike for example, can be suspended from two ceiling points.

The shelving system is fixed back to the wall substructure, on a 2184 mm module. The system comprises:

● inclined frame members, made up from two aluminium angles bolted back-to-back with stainless steel spacer 'pig-nosed' bolts
● horizontal frame members, also of back-to-back aluminium angles
● shelves of white cellulose-painted MDF
● shelf brackets of sprayed aluminium that hook over the spacer bolts at the front and are held by stainless steel rods.

The brackets have pairs of stainless steel lugs on either side. The shelves have rebates in the undersides to allow them to be located on the lugs. The system is loose-fit but rigid when assembled. It is also strong enough to take heavy exhibits, for example large hi-fi speakers. A major item such as a refrigerator can be placed on the plinth blocks that slide between the horizontal frame members and sit directly on the floor. These plinths are of painted MDF on a softwood frame. Their back edge locates in a slot between the top of a pre-cast concrete kerb that runs around the gallery and the bottom of the wall lining. This slot allows power cables to be run from power points in the floor to functioning exhibits.

The finishes in the gallery enhance its 'quiet' attitude. Walls and ceilings are painted matt white, and flooring is of a fine aggregate grey epoxy resin 'terrazzo' laid over the existing concrete slab. This gives a tough finish that can cope with heavy exhibits or temporary partitions being placed directly on to it without suffering damage. ■

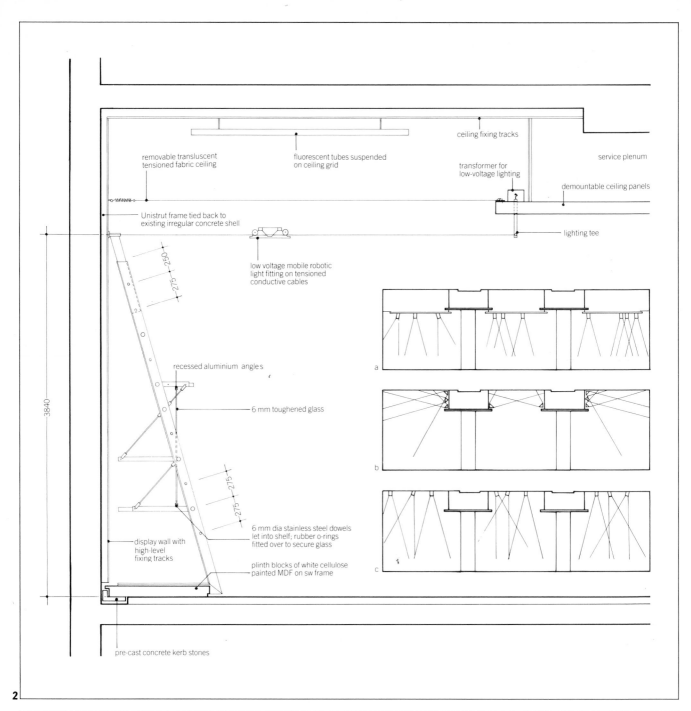

removable transluscent
tensioned fabric ceiling

fluorescent tubes suspended
on ceiling grid

ceiling fixing tracks

transformer for
low-voltage lighting

service plenum

demountable ceiling panels

Unistrut frame tied back to
existing irregular concrete shell

lighting tee

low voltage mobile robotic
light fitting on tensioned
conductive cables

250

275

3840

recessed aluminium angles

6 mm toughened glass

a

275 275

b

6 mm dia stainless steel dowels
let into shelf; rubber o-rings
fitted over to secure glass

display wall with
high-level
fixing tracks

plinth blocks of white cellulose
painted MDF on sw frame

c

pre-cast concrete kerb stones

2

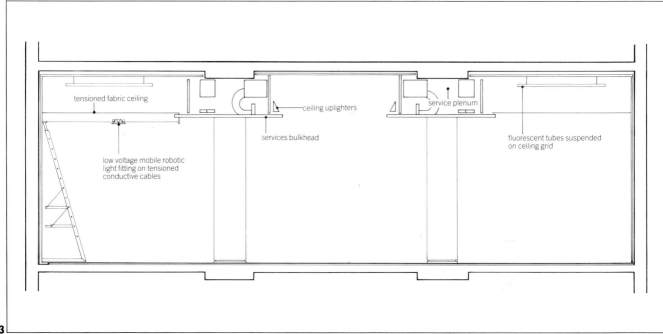

tensioned fabric ceiling

ceiling uplighters

service plenum

low voltage mobile robotic
light fitting on tensioned
conductive cables

services bulkhead

fluorescent tubes suspended
on ceiling grid

3

4

2 Part section through the review gallery showing shelving and lighting arrangements (inset). The lighting can be changed to suit a variety of conditions: a, diffused uplighting above the tensile ceiling with optional spotlights below; b, fluorescent fixed to rotating three-circuit track in bulkhead, achieves uniform wash to ceiling and walls; c, lighting from track in high-performance ceiling grid, with spots or floodlights on exhibits below.
3 Cross-section through the gallery showing servicing arrangements and alternative shelving option.
4 Shelving details. The shelves are held by stainless steel rods, either in tension or compression. When in compression, a stainless steel sleeve is fitted over the rod for reinforcement. For items that require limited protection, vertical pieces of glass can be fitted between the shelves.
5 Isometric shelving details; at the wall fixing point, top; typical bracket condition, middle; at floor level, bottom.

Credits
location Butlers Wharf, Shad Thames, London SE1
client The Conran Foundation
architect Conran Roche
architects (temporary exhibition gallery) Stanton Williams
quantity surveyor Davis Langdon & Everest
services, electrical/mechanical engineer YRME
structural engineer F. J. Samuely & Partners
main contractor Sir Robert McAlpine & Sons
subcontractors: services installation How Engineering, *structural systems* Unistrut (Southern) Ltd, *plasterboard ceilings* City Ceiling Systems, *epoxy resin flooring* Ryebrook Resins, *precast kerb sections* Diespecker, *gallery sliding doors* Beldon Doors, *timber wall lining* Pacific Interiors, *lighting* Erco, Concord, SKK, *tension fabric ceilings* Skycraft, *metalwork components* A. G. Parker Engineering, Symmonds Engineering, Marler Hayley, James Wheatley Enterprises, Goodings Aluminium, *shelving units* Carlton Beck.

Photo credit
Photographs by Peter Cook

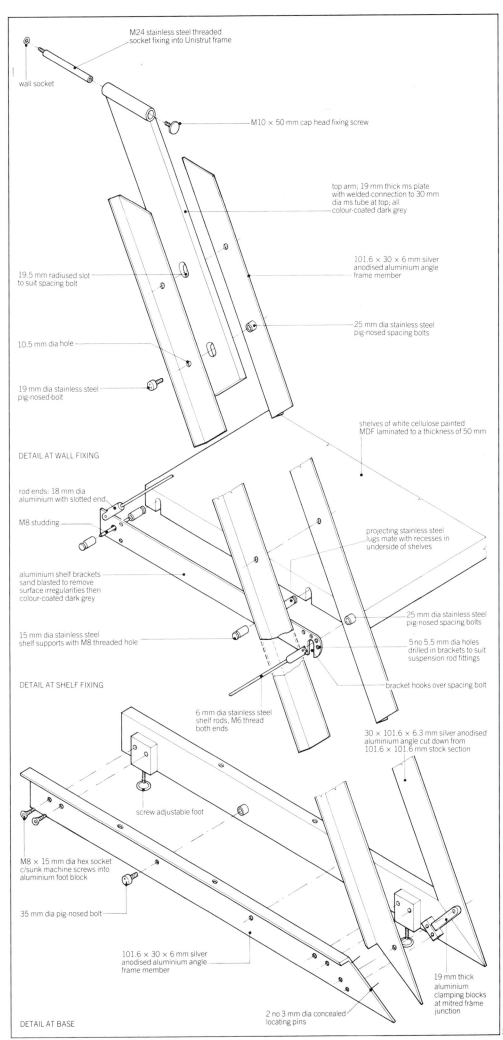

M24 stainless steel threaded socket fixing into Unistrut frame

wall socket

M10 × 50 mm cap head fixing screw

top arm; 19 mm thick ms plate with welded connection to 30 mm dia ms tube at top; all colour-coated dark grey

101.6 × 30 × 6 mm silver anodised aluminium angle frame member

19.5 mm radiused slot to suit spacing bolt

25 mm dia stainless steel pig-nosed spacing bolts

10.5 mm dia hole

19 mm dia stainless steel pig-nosed bolt

shelves of white cellulose painted MDF laminated to a thickness of 50 mm

DETAIL AT WALL FIXING

rod ends: 18 mm dia aluminium with slotted end

M8 studding

projecting stainless steel lugs mate with recesses in underside of shelves

aluminium shelf brackets sand blasted to remove surface irregularities then colour-coated dark grey

25 mm dia stainless steel pig-nosed spacing bolts

15 mm dia stainless steel shelf supports with M8 threaded hole

5 no 5.5 mm dia holes drilled in brackets to suit suspension rod fittings

DETAIL AT SHELF FIXING

bracket hooks over spacing bolt

6 mm dia stainless steel shelf rods, M6 thread both ends

30 × 101.6 × 6.3 mm silver anodised aluminium angle cut down from 101.6 × 101.6 mm stock section

screw adjustable foot

M8 × 15 mm dia hex socket c/sunk machine screws into aluminium foot block

35 mm dia pig-nosed bolt

101.6 × 30 × 6 mm silver anodised aluminium angle frame member

19 mm thick aluminium clamping blocks at mitred frame junction

2 no 3 mm dia concealed locating pins

DETAIL AT BASE

5